SNICKER
THE BROWNIE
AND
OTHER STORIES

Snicker the Brownie

and
Other Stories

by
ENID BLYTON

Illustrations by
VALERIE EWENS

AWARD PUBLICATIONS

ISBN 0 86163 146 3

Text copyright ©1944 Darrell Waters Limited
Illustrations copyright ©1985 Award Publications
Limited
First published as *Enid Blyton's Jolly Storybook*
by Hodder & Stoughton Ltd. 1944

This edition entitled
Snicker the Brownie and Other Stories
published 1985 by Award Publications Limited
Spring House, Spring Place, London NW5 3BH

Printed in the German Democratic Republic

CONTENTS

1

The Dumpy Wizard's Party

The Dumpy Wizard was just like his name – fat and round and dumpy. He was a nice old fellow, as merry as a blackbird, and he simply loved giving parties.

People loved going to his parties too! They were so jolly – always lots of nice things to eat and exciting games to play.

But the Dumpy Wizard was very particular about the people he invited to his parties. He wouldn't have anyone with bad manners. He wouldn't have anyone untruthful. He wouldn't have anyone greedy. So, if someone was left out of one of his parties, people always knew that there was something wrong with them just then.

Now one day Tricky the gnome was running down the street, and he turned the corner quickly. Bump! He banged right into Dumpy the Wizard, and they both fell over. Dumpy sat in a puddle. Tricky banged his head against a wall.

'What did you do that for?' roared Dumpy.

'What do you mean?' yelled back Tricky. 'You bumped into me as much as I bumped into you!'

'Why don't you look where you are going?' shouted Dumpy.

'I was, but you came where I was just about to go!' cried Tricky.

'Don't be silly,' said Dumpy, drying himself with his handkerchief.

'I'm not,' said Tricky.

'Oh yes, you are!' said Dumpy.

'Oh no, I'm not!' said Tricky.

'Oh yes, you are!' said Dumpy. 'I shan't ask you to my next party.'

'I shall come all the same – yes, and eat up your nicest jellies!' said Tricky.

'You won't,' said Dumpy.

'Oh yes, I will,' said Tricky.

'Oh no, you won't,' said Dumpy.

'Now then, move on you two,' said Blueboy, the policeman of the village. 'Stop quarrelling!'

So Tricky and Dumpy had to move on. Dumpy was quite sure he *wouldn't* let Tricky come to his party – and Tricky was quite sure he *would* go – and eat up the best jellies too!

Dumpy sent out his invitations – and do you know, *everyone* was invited this time – except Tricky, of course! He said *he* didn't care, not he! And in his cunning little head he made a plan.

It was to be a fine party. There was to be a record player going, and everyone was to sing and dance to it. There were to be four different coloured jellies –

9

green, red, orange and pink – and a fine cake with a rabbit in sugar on the top. Oooh!

The day soon came. Everyone put on their best clothes and looked as excited as could be. Only Tricky kept on his old clothes – but he didn't seem to care a bit – he just ran about as usual, humming and whistling as if *he* didn't care about parties.

Four o'clock came. Gnomes, goblins, brownies, and pixies crowded into Dumpy's little cottage. Only two people were not there – Tricky, of course – and Blueboy the policeman, who had to guard everyone's house because they were all empty.

The record player was set going. The dancing began. People sang as they danced. What a noise there was! Everyone was excited and happy, because, set out at the end of the room was a table full of good things. The four coloured jellies shivered and shook. The sugar rabbit on the iced cake stood up and looked with very sugary eyes at all the dancers. It was a very merry evening.

11

Just as everyone was feeling hungry, and thinking it was about time the dancing stopped and the eating began, there came a knock at Dumpy's front door.

Blim-blam!

'Who can that be?' said Dumpy, in surprise.

He opened the door. Outside stood someone dressed in a blue uniform, looking very stern.

12

'Hallo, Blueboy,' said Dumpy, in surprise. 'What do you want?'

'Have you any idea of the noise you are making?' said Blueboy, in a stern voice.

'Oh, we are only dancing and singing,' said Dumpy. 'We are not making much noise Blueboy.'

'And I say you *are!*' said Blueboy. 'I could hear it very plainly indeed from outside. You may not be able to hear what the noise is like from inside. It sounds really *dreadful* out here! You will wake everyone up!'

'But there is nobody to wake up,' said Dumpy. 'Everyone is here.'

'Don't argue with me, Dumpy,' said Blueboy, in such a cross voice that Dumpy was quite surprised. 'I tell you that the noise from outside is simply dreadful.'

'I'll come out and hear it,' said Dumpy. He turned round and called to his guests. 'The policeman says that the noise we are making sounds simply dreadful outside. I'm going to hear it.'

'You'd better *all* come and hear it!' said the policeman. 'Then you will believe what I say. Come along, everyone!'

Blueboy went into the house and pushed everyone out. He shut the door – and once the door was shut, he took off his big helmet – and he wasn't Blueboy at all! He was naughty Tricky, who had dressed up as a policeman to play a joke on Dumpy!

He emptied the four lovely jellies into his helmet, and snatched the sugar rabbit off the cake. Then he slipped quietly out of the kitchen door and ran out of the back garden, home! he had been to the party after all!

The people outside crowded together and listened to hear the dreadful noise that Dumpy's party was supposed to have been making. They listened – and they listened.

'I can't hear a sound!' said Gobo the pixie.

'Not a word!' said Tippy the gnome.

'The party isn't a bit noisy!' said Dumpy crossly. 'I don't know what Blueboy meant. Why, there might be nobody in the house, it's so quiet! There's not a sound to be heard!'

'Well,' said Happy the goblin, with a chuckle, 'there *is* nobody in the house now – except Blueboy! We've all come out – to listen to ourselves making a noise indoors! Ho, ho, ho!'

'Ho, ho, ho!' roared everyone – and really, it *was* very funny, wasn't it! They had all gone outside to listen to the dreadful noise they were making *inside*! Dear, dear, dear, whatever next!

'Come on in,' said Dumpy. 'We'll tell that silly old Blueboy we didn't hear a sound!'

15

So into the house they all went – but where was Blueboy? Nowhere to be found! And where were the four beautiful jellies? Nowhere to be seen! And where, oh, where was that lovely sugar rabbit? He was gone – and the kitchen door was wide open! Oh dear!

'That wasn't Blueboy, it was Tricky!' suddenly cried Dumpy. 'Yes, it was. I thought his voice wasn't Blueboy's. Oh, he has been to my party, as he said he would – and taken the best jellies – and my beautiful sugar rabbit too!'

'All because we were foolish enough to do what he told us – and leave the house to hear the noise we were making!' groaned Happy the goblin. 'I know, Dumpy – let me run to Tricky's cottage and tell him we've found out his trick – and it was really very funny, you know – and say he can come to the party if he brings back the jellies and the sugar rabbit.'

'All right,' said Dumpy. 'Go and tell him. He is too clever for me – I'd rather he was my friend than my enemy!

Goodness knows what he would make us do next!'

So Happy raced off to Tricky's cottage. Tricky had emptied the jellies out of his helmet on to a big dish and was just going to eat them.

'Hey, stop!' said Happy, running in, 'We want you to come to the party. That was a clever trick you played, Tricky - but don't make Dumpy unhappy about his jellies and sugar

rabbit. He was very proud of them!'

'Very well,' said Tricky, getting up. 'I'll come - and I'll bring the jellies and the rabbit with me!'

So back he went to the party with Happy - and everyone laughed and said he was a rascal, and Dumpy said he would forgive him if he wouldn't play any more tricks.

So they all settled down again, and the record player played, and the jellies were eaten, and the sugar rabbit was put back on the cake, where he looked simply splendid.

'It was a lovely party – even if the jellies *did* taste a bit helmety,' said Tricky, when he said goodbye to Dumpy.

'Well – that was *your* fault!' said Dumpy with a grin.

2

The Sneezing Donkey

Once upon a time there was a small grey donkey who lived in a farm field and ate the grass and the thistles there. As he wandered across the field he felt a tickling in his nose. He lifted up his head and sneezed.

'A-tish-ee-aw!' he sneezed. 'A-tish-ee-aw!'

His nose tickled again. He sneezed even more loudly. 'A-TISH-ee-aw!'

He blinked and looked round. He could quite well feel another sneeze coming. It came. 'A-TISH-EE-TISH-EE-TISH-EE-AW!' he went, so loudly that some geese nearby fled away in alarm.

The donkey looked round, and to his surprise it had begun to pour with rain.

'That was my big sneeze did that,' he thought to himself, pleased. 'I have made it rain. I am really very clever. I shall tell everyone what I have done.'

So he cantered over to the sheep and spoke to them. 'Sheep, listen to me. Do you see this pouring rain? Well, I made it come when I sneezed so loudly!'

'How clever you are!' said the sheep admiringly. 'Nothing happens when *we* sneeze!'

The donkey ran to the old brown horse and spoke to him too. 'Horse, listen to me. Do you see this pouring rain? Well, I made it come when I sneezed so loudly.'

'How clever you are,' said the horse admiringly. 'Nothing happens when *I* sneeze!'

The donkey did feel proud. He wondered who else he could tell. He saw the hens and the cock at the end of the field and he trotted over to them. They were sheltering under the big hedge.

'Hens and cock, listen to me. Do you

see this pouring rain? Well, I made it come when I sneezed so loudly!'

'How clever you are!' said the hens and the cock admiringly. 'Nothing happens when *we* sneeze – but then, we never *do* sneeze!'

The donkey swung his long tail about, and wondered if he could tell anyone else. He saw the farm dog lying down in his kennel and he cantered over to him.

'Rover, listen to me. Do you see this pouring rain? Well, I made it come by sneezing so loudly.'

'How clever of you!' said Rover admiringly. 'Nothing happens when *I* sneeze!'

The ducks came waddling by in a row, going to the pond. They were delighted with the rain. The donkey ran over to them.

'Ducks, listen to me,' he said. 'Do you see this pouring rain? Well, *I* made it come when I sneezed so loudly.'

'How clever of you!' said the ducks admiringly. 'Nothing happens when *we* sneeze – but how we'd like it to rain whenever we sneeze!'

The donkey was so pleased with himself that he simply didn't know what to do. The rain went on falling. It rained all day. It rained all night. It went on raining the next day too.

The sheep got tired of the rain. The brown horse got tired of the rain. The hens and cock got tired of the rain. Rover got tired of the rain. Everywhere was muddy. Everyone was wet and cold. Only the ducks liked the rain.

The sheep, the horse, the hens, cock and dog gathered together by the hedge and grumbled to one another.

'Look what that silly donkey has done with his sneezing! No one would have minded just a shower – but why

should he make it rain day and night like this? Let's go and tell him to stop the rain now.'

So they went to the donkey. He was standing under a tree thinking how marvellous it was to have sneezed so much rain down.

'Donkey, we are wet and cold. Stop this rain at once,' neighed the horse.

'Donkey, our feathers are dripping. Stop this rain,' clucked the hens and cock.

'Donkey, I have a feeling I shall bite

your long tail if you don't sneeze again and *stop* the rain!' barked Rover, who could be very fierce.

The donkey stared at everyone in alarm. It had been easy enough to begin the rain – but he wasn't at all sure he could stop it. Besides, he couldn't sneeze unless a sneeze came. Whatever was he to do?

'The ducks like the rain,' he said at last. 'If I stop the rain they will be angry and come and peck me.'

'Well, we will be angrier and we will bite you, and nibble you and peck you too!' cried all the animals and birds at once.

'I don't know how to sneeze unless a sneeze happens to come,' said the donkey, 'and I don't know how to stop the rain.'

'Well, why do you start a thing you don't know how to stop?' wuffed Rover crossly. 'I shall snap at each of your legs!'

'And I shall butt you with my head,' said the sheep.

'And I shall kick you with my heels,' said the horse.

'And we will peck you with our beaks,' said the birds. So they all began. They were so busy teasing the poor donkey that no one noticed that the clouds were blowing away – and the rain was stopping – and the sun was shining! But that was what was happening. The fields shone and glittered in the sun – it was a really lovely day.

'Stop! Stop!' cried the donkey. 'Don't you see the sun? Why are you teasing me like this? The rain has stopped! You ought to be ashamed of yourselves!'

The animals and birds looked round. The donkey was right. It was a beautiful day. The rain had certainly stopped. They all went off joyfully and left the donkey alone in his corner of the field.

'Next time I sneeze I won't say anything about it,' said the grey donkey. 'Not a single word. There's no pleasing some people! They all said I was so clever, too. Well, maybe I wasn't as clever as I thought I was!'

Next time he sneezed he was *so* surprised to find that no rain came. But *I'm* not surprised – are you?

3

The Adventurous Ball

There was once a big round ball. It was all colours – red, yellow, blue, and green, and it looked very jolly indeed when it bounced or rolled.

The other toys were rather impatient with the ball. They thought it a silly, dull creature. It could do nothing but bounce.

'What a life you lead!' said the sailing boat to the ball. 'Nothing but bounce, bounce, bounce! Look at me! *I*

go sailing on the river and on the pond.
I even go on the sea at seaside time!'

'And what about *me*?' said the toy
bus. 'When I'm wound up I go round
and round the nursery, and I carry
dolls, bears and rabbits for passengers!
I have a fine life!'

'And I fly up in the air and see all
kinds of things!' said the toy aeroplane.

'So do I!' said the kite. 'I fly above the
clouds and see birds up there, and get
as near to the sun as I can!'

'And we dolls get about a lot too,'
said the curly-haired doll. 'We get out
in prams – we are taken out to tea – we
do see the world! Poor, dull ball, you do

nothing but bounce. We are sorry for you.'

The ball felt sorry for himself too. He had never felt dull before the toys had said all this to him, but now he really did feel as if he led a miserable sort of life.

However, the time came when all that was changed, as you will hear. It happened that the children in whose nursery the toys lived went off to the seaside for a holiday, and with them they took most of their toys. The bus went, the dolls went, the aeroplane, and kite – and the ball. What fun!

And then the ball's adventures began. It had longed and longed for adventures, and it was surprised when it had some. It had been taken down to the beach and left on the sand whilst the children dug castles. Nobody noticed that the tide was coming up. No one noticed that the tide had reached the ball. And no one saw that it had taken away the ball when it began to go out again!

But it had! It bobbed the ball up and down on little waves, and took it right out to sea!

'Good gracious!' said the ball to itself. 'I might be a little boat, the way I am floating along! Wherever am I going?'

A fish popped up its head and spoke to the ball. 'Hallo, big round fellow! What news of the land have you?'

The ball was proud to be able to tell news. It told the fish all about the other

toys. Then the fish told the ball about the sea, and all the fishes and other sea-creatures in it. 'You are a bold, brave ball to go adventuring off by yourself like this,' said the fish. 'I do admire you!'

The ball bobbed on, prouder than ever. Soon a big white seagull swooped down and came to rest just by the ball. 'Hallo, big round fellow,' he said in surprise. 'I thought you might be food. How very bold of you to come adventuring on the sea like this!'

The ball felt proud – but it was a truthful ball. 'Well, as a matter of fact, I can't very well help this adventure,' he said. 'The sea took me away.'

'Tell me news of the land,' said the gull. So the ball told all about the other toys, and the gull then told him of the gulls, and of their seaweed nests, and young brown gull-babies. He told the ball of stormy days at sea. He showed him how he dived for fish. The ball was pleased and excited. How nice everyone was to him!

The ball floated on. The tide turned again and flowed into a big bay. The ball floated by a boat and stayed there for a while. The boat spoke to him and told him how he sometimes went out fishing, and how little boys and girls went rowing in him and used him for bathing. The ball had never known such a lot of things in his life. He would have stayed by the boat for a longer time, but a little wave came and took him away. He floated into a rock-pool, and there the crabs and shrimps swam up to him in admiration.

'What a fine big round fellow you are!' they said. 'Where do you come from? How brave of you to adventure all alone on the big, big sea!'

The ball bobbed in the pool and listened to the tales the crabs and shrimps told him. He heard about the children who came shrimping with a big net. He saw how the little crabs could bury themselves in the sand in two winks and not show even a leg. It was all very wonderful to the big ball.

When the tide went out again the ball went with it. It bobbed along merrily. Suddenly it saw a great big thing coming straight at it. Oh dear, oh dear

– it was an enormous steamer! The ball felt sure it would be squashed to bits – but at the last moment it bobbed to one side and the big steamer sailed on. 'Look! Look!' cried the people on the steamer, leaning over the side.

'There is a fine big ball, bobbing along all by itself!'

The ball was proud to be noticed by the people on the steamer. It bobbed after it for a long way but then got left behind. The tide took it once more and some great big waves curled over it and almost buried it. But it bobbed up gaily again, wondering what adventure it would have next.

As it floated along it saw a little boat with two children in. 'Look! Look! There's a beautiful big ball!' cried the boy. 'Let's get it!'

The boat was rowed after the ball. The boy leaned out and took it. He shook the water from it and showed it to his sister.

'Do you know Winnie, I believe it is our very own ball – the one we lost

yesterday!' said the boy. 'See the colours on it! I am quite sure it is our own ball!'

'So it is!' said the girl. 'I wonder where it has been all this time! I wish it could tell us it's adventures. I expect it has had such a lot, bobbing up and down on the sea.'

The children took the ball back to shore. There were all the other toys - the aeroplane, the bus, the dolls, the kite, and all the rest. How surprised they were to see the ball again!

'We saw you floating away!' cried the aeroplane. 'Where did you go?'

'Ah,' said the ball proudly. 'I'm a big round adventurous fellow, I am! I've talked with birds and fishes, crabs and shrimps – I've heard tales from boats – I've nearly been run down by a great steamer, and all the people on it saw me! You may think I'm a dull fellow and can do nothing but bounce – but you are mistaken – I can float too – and I've had more adventures than the whole lot of you put together!'

And after that, as you can imagine, none of the toys ever laughed at the ball again for being a dull fellow who could do nothing but bounce! He could tell more stories than anyone else – and he says he is going to float away again next year and have some more adventures. I wonder if he will!

4

Snicker the Brownie

There was once a mischievous brownie called Snicker. He was always playing tricks – and they were hardly ever nice tricks!

Once he filled Dame Snippy's sugar tin with salt, and she couldn't *think* why all her cakes tasted so nasty that week. You see, she put salt into them instead of sugar.

Another time Snicker put some treacle inside Mr Doodle's hat, and dear me, the time Mr Doodle had, trying to get his hat off his head when he met Mrs Trips out shopping! Yes – Snicker was a very mischievous brownie!

But one day he went too far. Just listen! He thought he would go out for a walk, and see what mischief he could find to do. So off he went, his hands in his pockets and his bright eyes darting everywhere.

Before long he came to Cuckoo Wood. He walked down a path that he didn't know very well, and came to a small cottage in the heart of the wood. Snicker wondered who lived there. He looked all round it – and there, lying on the wall, were two big black witch-cats, sleeping in the sun!

Now, witch-cats have very long black tails – and Snicker saw these tails and planned a very naughty trick. He would tie them together whilst the cats were asleep – and then what a shock they would get when they woke up!

So, very quietly, he tiptoed up to the sleeping cats. He took their long, long tails and he tied them carefully into a huge knot. The cats slept on peacefully.

But the old witch who lived in the cottage looked out of the window and saw what Snicker had done. She

banged at her window in rage – and the cats woke up! They leapt down from the wall in fright – and, of course, as their tails were tied together, they could not run away. One cat tried to go to the house, the other tried to run out of the gate – and neither of them could move an inch because their tails were tied together and held them tightly!

Snicker began to laugh – and then a most surprising thing happened! The cats' tails came off! Yes, they really did – and what is more, those tails wriggled away like snakes, out of the garden gate, past Snicker, and slid off into the wood.

'Meow! Meow!' cried the two cats, in dismay. 'We've lost our tails!'

The witch came running down the path. She was in a fine temper. Before Snicker could escape she took him by the shoulders and gave him a good shaking.

'You nasty, mischievous little brownie!' she cried. 'Now just you go after those tails and bring them back, or I'll turn you into a jumping frog! Do you hear?'

Snicker was frightened. He really hadn't meant the tails to come off. He had forgotten that the tails of witch-cats are very magic, and come off easily.

'I'm sorry,' he said to the witch. 'I'll go at once. Don't punish me. I'll go this very minute!'

'They leave a silvery trail behind them just like a snail does,' the witch told him. 'Bring those tails back tonight – or you'll find yourself a jumping frog!'

Snicker ran off. He saw the silvery trail the tails left and he followed it. Through the wood he went – and waded over a stream – and then across a buttercup field – and then up a very steep hill – and then down the other side – and then through a little village of toadstool houses. Dear, dear, what a long way those tails had gone!

At last the silvery trail came to an end. It stopped at the door of a small

44

crooked cottage, painted a peculiar yellow. Snicker didn't like the look of it. He knew a goblin lived there – and goblins who live in yellow houses are usually bad tempered. Why had the tails gone there? Oh dear!

Snicker knocked at the door. A goblin opened it. He had brown wrinkles like tram-lines across his forehead, and no chin at all. Snicker didn't like the look of him.

'Please,' he said, 'I've come for the tails.'

45

'Tails!' said the goblin crossly. 'What tails?'

'The tails that came here,' said Snicker. 'Please give them to me, or I'll be turned into a jumping frog!'

'How did they come off?' asked the goblin.

'I tied them together, and when the cats ran away, the tails pulled and came off,' said Snicker, going very red.

'Ho!' said the goblin. 'Then the tails don't belong to *you*. I shall keep them!'

He slammed the door. Snicker stood outside wondering what to do. He knocked again. 'Go away!' roared the goblin. Snicker went round to the back door. It was open. He peeped inside. The goblin was busy untying the two tails from their knot.

'Tails, come to me!' shouted Snicker. The goblin looked up, frowned angrily, and held on tightly to the wriggling tails, which were trying their hardest to go to Snicker. But he could not hold them – and, in a rage, he flung them at Snicker, saying, 'Take them, then –

and much good may they do you!'

The tails wriggled and flapped – and Snicker didn't like them at all. He turned to run away – but those tails fastened themselves to the back of him as he ran – and there was Snicker with two long black tails!

He couldn't get them off! They were growing on him! Wasn't it dreadful? The more he tried to tug them off the more he hurt himself, and at last, with tears running down his cheeks, he

made his way back again to the witch's cottage.

'I've brought the tails back,' he told her. 'Here they are – growing on me. Please take them off.'

'Oh, I don't want them after all,' said the witch. She pointed indoors. 'Look! My cats have both got nice long tails again. A gnome came by today selling tails, so I bought two. You can keep your tails now!'

'But I don't WANT the tails!' cried Snicker in dismay. 'I don't! I don't! Everyone will laugh at me if I go about with two tails – especially ones like these that wave about so! Oh, do please take them off!'

'No,' said the witch. 'It's a good trick to play on you, Snicker! It will make people laugh and laugh.'

'How unkind of you!' said Snicker.

'Well, you are always playing tricks yourself, and laughing at others,' said the witch. 'Now you know what it feels like to be laughed at. I hope you enjoy it!'

She slammed the door and left poor Snicker outside. The brownie went home – and how everyone laughed at him and his two waving tails! It was dreadful!

Snicker wore them until he met a wizard who knew how to take them away. He had to pay the wizard a silver sixpence – but oh, how glad he was to see those two tails packed into a sack and taken away on the wizard's shoulder. The tips just showed out of the neck of the sack, waving about in the air.

'Well, that's the last of *them*!' said Snicker. 'And they've taught me a lesson! I shan't play unkind tricks on anyone again – only just nice funny ones! It's not nice to be laughed at unkindly.'

If ever you meet a brownie called Snicker say 'Tails!' to him! If he goes red you'll know it's the brownie in this story.

5

The Little Old Donkey

Neddy was an old grey donkey. He belonged to Farmer Meadows, and he had lived with him for many, many years. Each day he took the milk round for the farmer, and stopped at the doors whilst the farmer asked what milk was wanted, and poured it out from the big cans on Neddy's back.

But now Neddy was old. He did not like to drag the cart that the farmer's wife sometimes went to market in. He did not like to carry Toddy, the man who borrowed him when he wanted to ride to the next town.

The cart was heavy and so was Toddy. The milk-cans did not weigh so much, and Neddy liked taking those round with his master. But his back was old and tired now, and he was sometimes cross when he found that he was being put into the cart, and knew that he would have to drag it and the farmer's big wife, right to market and back again.

The farmer was angry with him. 'Come come, Neddy!' he said. 'Do as you are told! If you cannot do your work, I must sell you!'

'He is getting old,' said Tilly, the farmer's servant-maid. 'He is as old as I am!'

'He won't be much use soon,' said the farmer. 'I'd better sell him and get another donkey. Perhaps Toddy would buy him.'

Neddy was sad to hear this. He loved the farm he had lived in, and he loved his master, though the farmer was sometimes impatient and cross. He did not want to be sold to Toddy, who would ride him hard, and feed him badly. He drooped his grey head and felt unhappy.

Now one morning the farmer was ill.

He could not get out of bed, and he lay there and groaned and grumbled to his wife.

'I'll have to spend a few days in bed,' he said. 'I twisted my back the other day, and it will have to get right.'

'What about the milk-round?' asked his wife. 'We can't let our customers go without their milk. I can't take it myself and Tilly must do the cooking.'

'Well, the milk will have to be wasted then,' said the farmer. 'There's no one to take it – and if there were, there is no one who knows the round and who would know which person to call on.'

So, to Neddy's surprise, no one came to take him on the milk-round that morning. Tilly had strapped the big milk-cans on his back, for she hadn't known that the farmer was ill – and the little old donkey stood by the front door, waiting for him to come.

When he didn't come, the donkey knew that he must be ill. So Neddy trotted off by himself. Why shouldn't

he go on the round? Didn't he know every customer? They all loved Neddy, and wouldn't they be pleased to buy their milk from him, even though the farmer was not with him? Of course they would, thought the little old donkey.

He trudged into the town. first he went to Mrs White's house and stamped on the pavement outside. Mary White, the little girl, saw him and called out to her mother:

'Here's Neddy with the milk – all alone Mother! Isn't he clever? How much do you want?'

The mother came to the door with a jug.

'Hee-haw!' said Neddy, which meant, 'How much milk?' The woman laughed and dipped her jug into the can. 'One litre,' she said, and put the money into the purse that Neddy always carried by the cans. Neddy went off again and came to the next customer's house. Nobody was there, and though the donkey stamped on the pavement, nobody came to the door. Neddy looked for the bit of rope that pulled the bell inside the house. He had often seen his master pull this. So he took it between his teeth and pulled – jingle-jangle went the bell inside the house, and Mr Brown came to the door. He *was* surprised to see Neddy all alone!

'Hee-haw!' said Neddy politely. Mr Brown dipped his jug in the can, paid over his money, and Neddy went on again. By this time a few children had gathered round him, for they all knew Neddy, and they guessed that he had come to sell his milk without his master.

'Clever old donkey!' they cried, patting him. 'Do you know your next customer Neddy?'

Of course he did! He stopped at
Mother Lucy's house and stamped
hard. The old woman came out with
her jug.

'Neddy's alone!' shouted the children.
'He's going round to all the customers
by himself! He knows everyone!'

'I always said he was a clever beast,'
said Mother Lucy, who was fond of the
donkey. She took the milk she wanted,
and put the money into the purse. Then
she gave Neddy a fine red carrot. He
said 'Hee-haw' again and moved off,

56

chewing it. This was a good treat!

Well, Neddy went to every customer that his master served in the town, and by the time he had finished his round, he had no milk left and the purse was full! He had had another carrot and a half-turnip, so he had done well.

He trotted off with the empty milk-cans, still chewing a bit of turnip. He cantered in at the farm gate and went to the kitchen door. Tilly would be there he knew, and would unstrap the milk-cans.

Tilly and the farmer's wife had been wondering where the old donkey had got to. They had hunted everywhere for him. The farmer had been cross when he had been told that Neddy had disappeared.

'He'll trot about the fields with that milk in the cans and upset it all!' he said.

Tilly heard the donkey's hooves, and she ran to the door. When she saw the empty milk-cans and peeped into the purse and saw it bursting with money, she could hardly believe her eyes! She unstrapped the cans, gave Neddy a lump of sugar, and ran to the farmer and his wife with the cans and the purse.

'See what your faithful old donkey has done for you!' she cried. 'He has gone on the milk-round himself, and has sold the milk and brought back the money! Never did there live such a donkey as that one! He's worth his weight in gold!'

The farmer could hardly believe what Tilly told him. He emptied the money on to the bed and counted it. It was even more than usual!

'Wife!' he said, 'that donkey is a fine fellow. Old he may be, and not wishful to carry heavy weights – but he's a

faithful creature, and I'll not sell him to anyone!'

Tilly ran down and flung her arms round Neddy's neck. 'You're not going to be sold!' she said. 'You're the best donkey in the world, and the master knows it!'

'Hee-haw!' said Neddy. He was very happy. Each day he went on the milk-round by himself, and so famous did he become that his master had many more customers than usual!

He is still going his rounds, though he is very old now – but the farmer kept his word, and has never sold him. I hope he never will, don't you?

6

The Toys Go to the Seaside

Once upon a time the goblin Peeko put his head in at the nursery window and cried, 'Who wants a day at the seaside?'

The toys sat up with a jerk. They were all alone in the nursery, for Tom

and Beryl, whose toys they were, had
gone away to stay at their Granny's.
The toys were really feeling rather dull.
A day at the seaside sounded simply
gorgeous!

'How do we go?' asked the pink
rabbit.

'By bus,' said the goblin grinning.
'*My* bus. I bought it yestereday. Ten
pence each all the way there.'

'Ooooh!' said the sailor doll, long-
ingly. 'I *would* like to see the sea. I've

61

never been there – and it's dreadful to
be a sailor doll and not know what the
sea is like, really it is!'

'Come on then,' said Peeko. 'Climb
out of the window, all of you. There's
plenty of room in the bus.'

So the pink rabbit, the sailor doll, the
yellow duck, the walking-doll, the black
dog, and the blue teddy bear all
climbed out of the window and got into
the goblin's bus, which was standing
on the path outside. The goblin took
the wheel. The bus gave a roar and a
jolt that sent the pink rabbit nearly
through the roof – and it was off! It was
a fine journey to the sea. The goblin
knew all the shortest cuts. It wasn't
long before sailor doll gave a yell and
cried, 'The sea! The sea!'

'Pooh!' said the goblin. 'That's just a
duck-pond.'

'But aren't those gulls sailing on it?'
asked the doll.

'No, *ducks*!' said Peeko.

'Quack, quack!' said the yellow toy
duck, and laughed loudly at the sailor

doll. After that the doll didn't say anything at all, not even when they came to the real sea and saw it glittering and shining in the sun. He was afraid it might be a duck-pond too – or an extra big puddle!

They all tumbled out of the bus and ran on to the beach. 'I'm off for a swim!' said the yellow duck.

'I'd like a sail in a boat!' said the sailor doll. 'Oh! There's a nice little boat over there, just my size.'

It belonged to a little boy. He had gone home to dinner and had forgotten to take his boat with him. The sailor doll ran to it, pushed it out on to the sea, jumped aboard and was soon off for a fine sail. He *was* enjoying himself!

The pink rabbit thought he would like to make himself a burrow in the sand. It was always so difficult to dig a burrow in the nursery. Now he really would be able to make one! So he began to dig, and showered sand all over the blue teddy bear.

'Hey, hey, pink rabbit, what are you

doing?' cried the bear. But the pink rabbit was already deep in a sandy tunnel, enjoying himself thoroughly, and didn't hear the bear's shout.

'I shall have a nap,' said the blue teddy bear. 'Don't disturb me, anybody.'

He lay down on the soft yellow sand and shut his eyes. Soon a deep growly snore was heard. The black dog giggled and looked at the walking-doll. 'Shall we bury him in sand?' he wuffed. 'He would be so surprised when he woke up and found himself a sandy bear.'

'Yes, let's,' said the doll. So they began to bury the sleeping teddy bear in sand. They piled it over his legs, they piled it over his fat little tummy, they piled it over his arms. They didn't put any on his head, so all that could be seen of the bear was just his blunt blue snout sticking up. He did look funny.

'I'm off for a walk,' said the walking-doll. 'This beach is a good place to stretch my legs. I never can walk very far in the nursery – only round and round and round.'

She set off over the beach, her long legs twinkling in and out. The black dog was alone. What should he do?

'The sailor doll is sailing. The yellow duck is swimming. The pink rabbit is

burrowing. The teddy bear is sleeping.
The walking-doll is walking. I think I
will go and sniff round for a big fat
bone,' said the black dog. So off he
went.

Now when Peeko the goblin came on
to the beach two or three hours later, to
tell the toys that it was time to go
home, do you think he could see a
single one? No! There didn't seem to be
anyone in sight at all! Peeko was
annoyed.

'Just like them to disappear when it
it's time to go home,' he said crossly.
'Well, I suppose I must just wait for
them, that's all. I'll sit down.'

Peeko looked for a nice place to sit.
He saw a soft-looking humpy bit of
sand. It was really the teddy bear's
tummy, buried in sand, but he didn't
know that. He walked over to the
humpy bit and sat right down in the
middle of it.

The blue bear woke up with a jump.

'Oooourrrrrrr,' he growled, and sat
up suddenly. The goblin fell over in a

fright. The bear snapped at him and growled again. Then he saw it was Peeko.

'What do you mean by sitting down on the middle of me like that?' he said crossly.

'How should I know it was the middle of you when you were all buried in sand?' said Peeko.

'I wasn't,' said the bear, in surprise, for he had no idea he had been buried.

'You were,' said Peeko.

'I wasn't,' said the bear.

'Well, we can go on was-ing and wasn't-ing for ages,' said Peeko. 'Just tell me this, teddy – where in the world has everyone gone to? It's time to go home.'

'Is it really?' said the bear, astonished. 'Dear me, it seems as if we've only just come!'

'I don't see why you wanted to come at all if all you do is to snore,' said Peeko. 'Waste of a ten pence I call it!'

'Well if you think that, I won't give you my money,' said the teddy crossly.

'Don't be silly,' said the goblin. 'Look here bear, if we don't start soon it will be too late. What am I to do? I'd better go without you.'

'Oh no, don't do that,' said the bear in alarm. 'I'll soon get the others back. We have a special whistle that we use when it's time to go home.'

He pursed up his teddy-bear mouth and whistled. It was a shrill, loud whistle, and every one of the toys heard it. You should have seen them rushing back to the beach!

The sailor doll sailed his ship proudly to shore, jumped out, and pulled the ship on to the sand. He really did feel a sailor now!

The yellow duck came quacking and swimming in, bobbing up and down in

delight. She waddled up the beach, and shook her feathers, sending a shower of drops all over Peeko, who was most annoyed.

The walking-doll tore back across the beach. The black dog came running up, carrying an enormous bone in his mouth, very old and smelly. The toys looked at it in disgust.

'Where's the pink rabbit?' asked Peeko. 'He *would* be last!'

The toys giggled. Peeko was standing just at the entrance of the pink rabbit's burrow, but he didn't know he was! The toys knew what would happen – and it did!

The pink rabbit had heard the bear's whistling. He was coming back along his burrow. He suddenly shot out, all legs and sand – and Peeko felt his legs bumped hard, and he sat down very suddenly! The pink rabbit had come out in a great hurry, just between the goblin's legs. The toys laughed till they cried. Peeko was quite angry.

'First I sit on a hump that isn't a

hump and get a dreadful fright!' he said. 'And then I get bowled over by a silly rabbit who comes out of the sand. Get into the bus all of you, before I say I won't take you home.'

They all got into the bus. Most of them were tired and sleepy now, all except the teddy bear, who was very lively indeed – but then, he had been asleep all the time!

They climbed in at the nursery window. They each gave Peeko ten pence, and he drove his bus away quietly, and parked it under the lilac bush. The toys crept into the cupboard and sat as still as could be.

And when Tom and Beryl came back the next day from their Granny's they *were* surprised to see how well and brown their toys all looked.

'Just as if they had been to the sea!' said Tom.

'Don't be silly Tom!' said Beryl.

But he wasn't silly. They *had* been to the sea!

7

The Great Big Fish

Ellen and Donald ran to the pier. Mother had given them tenpence each to go on. It would be fun to run right out to the end and see the deep green sea there.

'We might see a big fish too,' said Ellen. 'Oh, I do wish we had a fishing-rod like all the fishermen on the pier have, Donald. I would so like to fish and catch a great big enormous fish!'

'I believe these fishermen are going in for a fishing match,' said Donald, as the two ran along the pier. 'There are so many of them today!'

It was quite true. The fishermen were fishing that day for a prize – five pounds was offered to the man who caught the biggest fish.

The children looked in the baskets of all the fishermen as they passed. No one had caught a fish yet.

Suddenly they came to old Mr Brown. He lived next door to them and was the kindest old man you can imgine. He often gave them money and sweets, and once he had brought them a fine Easter egg full of tiny chocolate eggs and two yellow fluffy chicks.

'Have you caught a fish yet?' asked Ellen, stopping to talk to him.

'Not yet,' said old Mr Brown. 'I haven't had much luck lately. I think all the fish must know my line too well!'

The children had a grand time on the pier. They looked at all the funny machines there and wished they had money to put in them. They watched the fishermen as they saw one after another pull up some fine fish. Old Mr Brown caught one too, but it was very tiny.

Then he pulled excitedly at his line and cried, 'I've got a big one this time!'

His rod bent till it almost broke – and then the line reeled up – and what do you suppose he had caught? A big old boot that had once belonged to a fisherman! How everyone laughed.

Mr Brown was disappointed. So were the children. The old man cut away the boot, and it fell back into the sea with a splash. Then he put fresh bait on his hook, and threw the line out again.

He waited and waited and waited. The children had their lunch with

them, so they sat down by him and waited too. But although the other fishermen caught many fish, old Mr Brown couldn't seem to catch any more at all.

'I'm quite stiff with sitting here so long,' he said at last. 'I think I'll go for a trot round the pier and back again children. Do you mind staying by my rod whilst I go?'

'May I hold it for you, do you think?' asked Donald eagerly. 'I've never held a rod in my life. I'll be very careful.'

So kind old Mr Brown let him hold the rod. Then off went the old man trotting round the pier to stretch his legs. Ellen stood by Donald and watched the water into which the line disappeared.

And then suddenly a most surprising and exciting thing happened! The rod Donald was holding almost flew out of his hands! It was a good thing he had such a tight hold of it!'

'It's a fish, a fish!' yelled Donald. 'Mr Brown, where are you, where are you?'

But Mr Brown was right down at the end of the pier. Ellen caught hold of the rod too. 'Wind this little wheel like Mr Brown does!' she said to Donald. So he wound in the line, and the fish on the end tried its best not to come with the line. It pulled and jerked – but Donald held it fast.

Another fisherman came to help, but Donald said he could manage. Ellen leaned over the pier-railings and squealed in excitement. 'I can see the fish, I can see it! It's a most enormous big one! Ooooh!'

Mr Brown appeared again, and as soon as he saw what was happening he rushed to Donald. He took his rod and began to play the fish – letting the line run out when the fish pulled very hard and reeling it in when he had a chance.

At last he had the fish. Another man had to catch it in a net as it came on to the pier, for it was so big.

The children were so excited that they could not stand still but jumped up and down all the time.

'Mr Brown, Mr Brown, your fish is the very biggest!' they shouted. 'Oh, how much do you think it weighs?'

It was weighed on the scales, and it was eleven pounds. Mr Brown was so

pleased. No one had caught such a big fish so far. Perhaps someone would catch a bigger one before the day was out. He would have to wait and see.

The children waited too. Every time a fisherman caught a fish they rushed to see how big it was – but no one caught such a big one as old Mr Brown.

At five o'clock, when the match ended, Mr Brown was given the prize of five pounds. He was so pleased that he simply couldn't stop smiling.

'You've had no tea,' he said to the children. 'You've been two big bits of luck for me, haven't you? Come along, and we'll go home and show this fine fish to everyone – then we'll go and have a nice tea together in a tea-shop.

We'll have shrimp sandwiches, chocolate cream buns, and two ice-creams each!'

So off they all went, and how everyone stared in surprise at the great big fish they carried! Mother said of course they could go to tea with Mr Brown, so they set off together to the tea-shop. They all ate a most enormous tea, and Donald and Ellen thanked Mr Brown very much and said they had never had such a lovely day in all their lives.

'Oh, it isn't finished yet!' said Mr
Brown, beaming all over his red shining
face. 'You've got to have a bit of my
prize you know, for you helped to catch
the big fish! Now, what do you think
you'd like, Ellen? A big doll? And you,
Donald? A box of soldiers?'

'I'd like a little fishing-rod, please,'
said Donald, 'and Ellen would like one
too. We would so like to go fishing
ourselves!'

'Right!' said Mr Brown. So he bought
them both a fine fishing-rod each, and
then they went home to bed, carrying
their new rods very proudly indeed.

Tomorrow they are going fishing on
the pier. I wish I could be there, too, to
see the very first fish they catch, don't
you?

8

Hallo, Sooty Face!

Peter Penny was a house-painter. He was a mischievous little pixie, always ready with a cheeky answer, and always whistling the latest pixie song. He was a clever house-painter, so people put up with him.

That spring he was very, very busy. He painted the doors and windows of Brownie Longbeard's house a beautiful blue. Longbeard was very pleased – until he found that Peter Penny had painted his chimneys blue too, which made his roof look very queer indeed.

Peter Penny painted the walls of Dame Hoppy's dining-room a pale green, the colour of primrose leaves, and she too, was very pleased – until she found that Peter Penny had painted her new Sunday bonnet green too, that

she had left on the dining-room table
one day.

Peter Penny also painted the gates
that led to Wizard Heigho's castle. He
painted them red and yellow in stripes
and they looked very grand; but
Heigho *was* cross when he found that
Peter Penny had also painted his pony
red and yellow as well. But Peter had
gone off to the next town by that time,
his money in his pocket, and his
cheeky mouth pursed up whistling, 'A
fairy loved a pixie who was very bright
and tricksy,' the latest song in Fairy-
land just then.

'Any work to do here?' he asked the
people he met. 'I'm Peter Penny the
painter. I'm clever at painting walls,
windows, doors, gates – anything you
like.'

'Well, it's getting late in the year for painting now,' said the villagers. 'It's July you know; most people have finished their cleaning and their painting.'

'You might try at old Witch Sharp-eye's' said a gnome. 'She was saying the other day that she really must get her house done again, for she was away all spring and didn't have anything done to it.'

'I'll try there,' said Peter Penny, and he skipped off to Witch Sharpeye's house. It stood on a hill, and was certainly in need of a coat of paint.

Peter Penny knocked at the door – rat-a-tat-tat, rat-a-tat-tat, rat-a-tat-*tat*!

'Stop that noise!' called a cross voice. 'One knock is enough.'

'Any house-painting needed, Mam!' called Peter Penny, sticking his cheeky head in at the door.

'Not if you knock like that,' said Witch Sharpeye, who was sitting in a rocking-chair, knitting at a long, long stocking. Round her sat twelve black cats, all watching her very solemnly.

'Your walls need a coat of paint,' said Peter Penny. 'Let me give them a coat of pale pink wash, and pick out your windows and doors in a soft blue, to match the blue and pink hydrangeas that are growing so beautifully in your garden, Madam.'

'That's a good idea,' said the witch, knitting away. 'How much do you charge?'

'A piece of gold to you, Mam,' said Peter.

'Cheap enough, if you do your work well,' said the witch. 'Begin tomorrow – but a word in your ear, Peter Penny. Be polite to my cats, or I'll know the reason why!'

'MIAOW!' said all cats together. Peter Penny bowed to them. 'The same to you!' he said.

The next day he began his work. He matched his paint with the lovely pink and blue hydrangeas and soon the dirty walls and windows began to look really beautiful.

Peter Penny would have been quite happy in his work if it hadn't been for the twelve cats. They all came to watch him at his job, and he didn't like it.

'Shoo!' he said. 'Shoo!'

But they wouldn't shoo. They just sat and watched him very solemnly, and if he did so much as a stroke of his brush wrong, they all spoke together in chorus.

'MIAOW! MIAOW!'

'Oh, go and chase your tails!' said Peter Penny, and flicked a spot of pink paint at the nearest cat. It caught it on the nose. The cat was offended and licked *off* the paint. It tasted so horrid that the cat hung its mouth open and looked disgusted. Peter Penny laughed.

But the cats would not go away. No, they sat round and watched Peter Penny at work, and if he sang or whistled too loudly, they all opened

88

their mouths and cried, 'MIAOW! MIAOW!' till they drowned Peter Penny's cheerful little voice and he had to be quiet.

Peter Penny soon finished his work. The witch's house looked very nice. She paid him a piece of gold and told him to clear up his things and take them away as she was going out that morning, and wanted him to be gone by the time she came back.

Peter Penny watched her go down the road to catch the bus. He grinned to himself.

He mixed up a pot of pink paint and a pot of blue paint. Then he went into the kitchen and shut the door. The twelve cats were there. Peter Penny was very, very naughty. He painted each cat's tail blue and cat's head pink. How strange and peculiar they looked when he had finished!

'There!' said Peter Penny. 'That is for watching me as if I were a mouse, all the time I was painting. The witch will get a shock when she comes in!'

But it was Peter Penny who got the shock – for the witch had missed the bus and had come back home again! Yes, really! She walked in at the door and stared in horror at her twelve black cats, all with pink heads and blue tails.

'So this is how you finish your jobs, is it!' she said to Peter Penny, who looked frightened. 'I've heard of your tricks before Peter Penny. Now you will just come with me and get some soot to make my cats black again.'

'I d-d-d-don't know where any s-s-soot is,' stammered Peter Penny.

'Well *I* do!' said the witch. 'The goblin sweeps always store their soot in the middle of poppies. You can just take a bag and come with me. You will look into every poppy you see, and if there is black soot there, you will put it into your bag and bring it home for my cats.'

Poor Peter Penny! The witch gave him a sack, and took him by the collar. She marched him into the fields where

great red poppies grew, and every time he came to a poppy the witch stuck his head into it for him to see if there was any black soot there.

And as there always was, Peter Penny's face became blacker and blacker and blacker! He spluttered and choked, but it was no use – he had to look into the middle of every single poppy. Then he had to shake the soot into his bag.

By the time it was full Peter Penny's face was black all over. He did look dreadful!

The witch marched him back to her house and made him mix the soot with some magic water. Then he had to

paint the cats' faces and tails black
again. It took him a long time.

'Now go and wash your face in this
water,' said the witch, handing him a
bowl in which was some strange-
looking water, silvery-grey. Peter Penny
tried to wash his face in it: but alas for
him there was magic in the silver
water, and it made his face stay black
so that he could not wash the soot off!

'You like to make things what they
shouldn't be!' said Witch Sharpeye,
'and now you've got a taste of what it
feels like. Your face shouldn't be black
– but it is – and it will be for a long time!
Ho, ho!'

Peter Penny went very red, but you
couldn't see the red because his cheeks
were black. He ran out of the house in a
rage.

Nobody would let him paint their
houses any more because he looked so
dirty with his black face. So he had to
turn himself into a sweep, and he
always puts his soot into the poppies,
just as the other sweeps do. You will

find it there if you look. Don't forget.

And now nobody remembers that Peter Penny was once Peter Penny, a rosy-cheeked little pixie. They all call him Sooty Face! He won't answer, but it makes no difference.

'Hallo Sooty Face!' everyone cries, as he goes down the road. 'Hallo, Sooty Face!'

Won't he be pleased when the spell works off and he can wash himself clean!

9

Nippy the Pixie

Nippy the pixie was a tiresome fellow. He had long strong fingers, and he loved to nip and pinch people with them. He had long toes, and he liked to kick slyly under the table. He liked to poke people too, and to tread on their toes. He was not a very pleasant chap.

One day he was very pleased. He had an invitation to a party! It was to be a seaside party, and Nippy thought that would be most exciting. Scaly the merman had asked him to the party. Nippy felt sure he would have a fine time.

He dressed himself in his best, got on his bicycle, and rode off. It wasn't very far to the sea. He would be at the party just in time!

Scaly was there to greet him. He shook hands politely, and asked Nippy

into his rock-pool, which was most beautifully decorated with seaweed and anemones.

Nippy dipped his hands into the water, rubbed them over his face, and muttered a few magic words. He could now go under the water without being wet! He could breathe there too. It was a marvellous spell.

Nippy followed Scaly into the pool. The seaweed fluttered round. The shells made a pretty floor, laid in a neat pattern over the sand. There was a table made of rock, and on it were all sorts of exciting things to eat!

'Where are the other guests?' asked Nippy, looking round.

'They will be here in a minute,' said Scaly; and, sure enough, they all swam up or crawled up as he finished speaking.

They were strange guests. There was a large yellow crab, and there were three small green crabs. There was a great lobster, a rather alarming fellow. There were six shrimps and six prawns,

all neat and shining. There was a fat jellyfish with ribbons hanging down from his umbrella-like body. Nippy didn't much like the look of them.

They all knew Nippy. They shook hands with him, and nodded. 'Ah, Nippy!' they said. 'We have heard of you! Yes – we have heard of you!'

Nippy felt rather pleased. He hadn't known he was so famous!

'Pray sit down!' said Scaly, the merman, beckoning his guests to the rock-table, on which were sea-cakes, seaweed lemonade, sea-spray ice-cream with foam on the top, and rock-biscuits, hard outside and sweet inside.

Everyone sat down. Nippy sat next to one of the little green crabs. Opposite him was the lobster. Nippy looked hungrily at the cakes. He pinched the little crab next to him in excitement. 'Isn't this fun!' he said.

The crab opened a pair of his pincers and pinched Nippy back. 'Oooh!' said Nippy, startled. 'Don't do that. It hurts!'

'But you did it to me,' said the crab smiling, and looking at Nippy with his stalked eyes. 'It's a fine game, this nipping and pinching. That's why Scaly asked you to his party – you are the only pixie he knows who can nip and pinch and poke as we can. He thought you would enjoy it very much.'

'Oh,' said Nippy, feeling rather alarmed.

The big lobster opposite beamed at him and put a pair of his enormous claws under the table. He felt about for Nippy's bare knee and nipped it hard.

'Ooooh!' said Nippy. 'Don't!'

'You can nip me back,' said the lobster. 'Go on Nippy, pinch me hard.

We love it you know.'

'*We* like poking people with the sharp needles in our heads,' said a large prawn suddenly to the pixie. 'Like this Nippy!'

The prawn dug the surprised pixie in the chest with his sharp needle, and Nippy gave a yell and fell off his chair. Another shrimp poked him hard. Then the big yellow crab pinched each of his toes in turn. What fun those creatures had!

'I don't like it, I don't like it!' wept Nippy. 'Please stop them, Scaly.'

'But this is their idea of fun,' said the merman. 'I thought it was yours too, Nippy. I have often heard how you pinch, nip, kick, and poke people, so I thought you'd love my party. Please don't spoil it. Go and nip everyone else. Crabs and lobsters love that kind of game.'

'But they are so hard to nip!' wept Nippy. 'And they can nip me much harder than I can nip them. It isn't fair.'

Just at that moment the jellyfish left its place and floated over to Nippy. 'Play with me pixie,' it said, in a soft, shivery voice. It let down its ribbon-streamers all round the pixie, and Nippy gave a yell.

'You're stinging me, you're stinging me!' he cried. 'Go away!'

'Come on, boys, let's have a fine game with this silly pixie!' cried the big lobster. And, to Nippy's horror, all the shrimps, prawns, crabs, lobster, and jellyfish surrounded him and began to have a horrid sort of game with him. They pinched him and nipped him and pricked him and poked him and stung him till Nippy rushed out of the pool, jumped on his bicycle, and rode back home, crying bitterly.

'It was a horrid, horrid party!' he wept. 'Scaly was silly to think I'd like a pinching party with all those sea-creatures!'

He sat down at home and made himself a cup of cocoa and took some biscuits from a tin, for he had had no tea at all. He thought hard as he nibbled and drank.

'I hated that pinching and poking,' he thought. 'How other people must have hated *my* pinching and poking too! I'll never do it again, never!'

He didn't tell anyone about Scaly's pinching party, but they all knew – because Scaly told them! How they laughed and laughed!

'Nippy won't try his old tricks again!' they said. And he didn't. He keeps his fingers to himself now – and a good thing too! If you know anyone who is a pincher or poker, just let Scaly know – he'll arrange a nice little party for them, you may be sure!

10

Granny's Lovely Necklace

Granny, Mummy, Daddy, Eileen and Jim were all down by the sea. It was such fun! The weather was fine and sunny, the sea was blue and the sands were smooth and yellow.

Granny was very happy. She did like being with everyone she loved. Eileen and Jim were very kind to her, because really she was the sweetest old lady you could imagine. She was always diving into her big bag for sweets, or cakes, or apples for Eileen and Jim, and she was always ready to listen to all they said or to tell them stories about the exciting things she did when she was a little girl.

Granny had a lovely necklace which she nearly always wore. It was made of shiny crystal beads with pretty blue ones here and there. Mummy and Daddy had given it to her for a birthday present, and Granny was very proud of it. Once she let Eileen wear it for a whole afternoon, and Eileen felt as grand as could be.

One day Granny lost her necklace. She simply couldn't *think* where it had gone. She felt for it round her neck - and it wasn't there!

'Oh dear, oh dear!' she said, in alarm. 'My necklace is lost! Eileen! Jim! Tell me, can you see my lovely necklace round my neck or anywhere on me at all?'

Eileen and Jim looked - but there was no shining necklace to be seen.

'Granny, it must have dropped off your neck when we went out in the boat this morning,' said Jim suddenly. 'You know, I thought I heard something fall into the water, and I thought it was my knife - but it must have been your necklace. I felt for my knife, and it was safely in my pocket.'

'Oh dear, do you really think it fell into the sea?' said poor Granny. 'Well, it's lost for good then. I shall never find it again. I am so sad about it.'

Granny looked so unhappy that Eileen and Jim felt unhappy too. They knew how horrid it was to lose any-

105

thing they really liked. Once Jim had
lost his favourite blue pencil and once
Eileen had lost her second best doll –
and they had both worried all day long.

Mummy and Daddy were told about
the necklace. They were very sorry too.

'You had it on when you got into the
boat this morning with the children,'
said Mummy. 'I remember seeing it
flash in the sun. Yes, Granny dear –
you must have dropped it overboard
when you leaned over to look at the fish
or something.'

'Well, it's gone now,' said Granny. 'I
must just put up with it.'

That afternoon Jim and Eileen were
to go off for a picnic with Mummy, and
they were going to leave Daddy to play
golf and Granny to read by herself. But
somehow the children didn't like going
off to enjoy themselves when Granny
was feeling rather upset.

'Let's put off the picnic till tomorrow,'
said Jim to Eileen. 'I know what we'll
do, Eileen – we'll get out our big
shrimping net and we'll go shrimping

to see if we can catch lots of shrimps for Granny's tea. You know how she loves shrimps. That will be a treat for her to make up for her lost necklace.'

'That's a good idea, Jim' said Eileen. 'I'll fetch the net. I know where it is.'

Jim told Mummy about his idea. Mummy was pleased because she thought it was kind of the children. 'Granny won't be alone for tea if we don't go for a picnic,' she said. 'And *won't* she be pleased to have a feast of shrimps!'

Eileen and Jim went off with their net. The tide was coming in. 'It will bring the shrimps with it!' said Jim. 'I do hope there will be lots of big ones.'

They took off their shoes and stockings and ran to the edge of the water. They had seen the fisher-girls with their enormous nets shrimping at a certain place on the beach, and they guessed that was good for shrimps. They began to push the net lightly over the surface of the sand, a little way in the water.

'You can have a turn first, Eileen,' said Jim. 'I'll carry the basket.'

So Eileen had a turn first. The little waves curled round her legs. They were warm and tickly. Eileen liked to feel them. She pushed the net along, hoping there would be lots of shrimps in it when she looked.

'Have a look now,' said Jim. So Eileen lifted up the net carefully.

'Oooh! Oooh! Look at them jumping!' cried Jim in delight. 'You *have* caught a nice lot, Eileen! Let's put them into the basket.'

They put them into the basket. There were eleven! Six of them were so big that they really almost looked like prawns.

'Now your turn, Jim,' said Eileen. She gave him the shrimping net, and took the basket. Jim pushed the net along the sand eagerly. It was such fun to shrimp. He did hope he would catch as many shrimps as Eileen.

'I'll look and see how many I've got now,' he said at last. He lifted up the net – but will you believe it, there was only one tiny green crab in the net! Not a single shrimp jumped there! Jim was so disappointed.

'Have another turn, Jim,' said Eileen generously. But Jim shook his head.

'No,' he said, 'it's your turn, Eileen. I've had mine. I'll have another in a minute.'

So Eileen had a second turn – and do you know, when she lifted up the net again she had fourteen shrimps! They were nearly all big ones. She could hardly believe her eyes.

'I really am lucky,' she said to Jim, as they emptied the shrimps into the basket. 'Now your turn again, Jim.'

Poor old Jim! He didn't catch any

shrimps when he had his second turn either – and not even a crab – only a big piece of seaweed. He was dreadfully disappointed. He couldn't think why he was so unlucky.

'Perhaps you push the net too deeply into the sand and frighten away the shrimps before they get into the net,' said Eileen. 'I'll have my third turn now. I wonder if I'll catch any more!'

Eileen was certainly lucky that afternoon. She caught forty-three shrimps

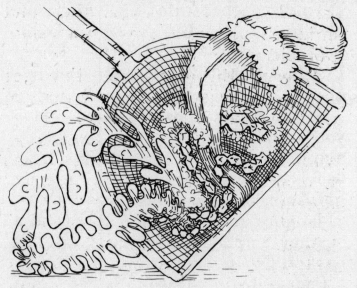

altogether, though poor Jim didn't catch one. But he caught something much better. Listen!

He was having his last turn. He lifted up the net to see if he had got a shrimp *this* time – and he saw something glittering in the net. Whatever do you think he had caught? Guess!

He had caught Granny's beautiful necklace! What do you think of that? The tide had brought it in to shore and it was lying half-buried in the sand at the edge of the waves. Jim had shrimped just there – and the necklace had slid into his net.

'Eileen! Eileen! Look, I've got Granny's necklace!' shouted Jim, in great excitement. 'Oh, do look!'

'Jim! Oh, how lovely! What a surprise! Whatever will Granny say!' cried Eileen in delight. 'Quick! Let's go and tell Mummy.'

So off they ran. Mummy was simply delighted. 'I know what we'll do,' she said. 'I'll cook the shrimps for tea and we'll put them into a covered dish – and

111

we'll wash the necklace and put that into a covered dish, too – and we'll tell Granny that you've each caught her something for tea! Won't she be excited!'

So at tea-time there were two covered dishes on the table. 'I caught you what's in *that* one!'

Granny opened the first dish. It was full of delicious shrimps.

'Oh how lovely!' she cried. 'What *can* be in the other dish?'

She took the cover off – and when she saw her lovely necklace glittering there, she could hardly believe her eyes!

'My necklace!' she said joyfully. 'Oh, my lovely necklace! Children, do please tell me how you found it.'

So they told her how they had given up their picnic to catch her some shrimps for tea – and how Eileen had caught her such a lot of shrimps – and Jim none – and then how he had caught the glittering necklace!

'You are two good, kind children,' said Granny, hugging them both. 'You have given me two beautiful surprises, and now it is my turn to give *you* one! I shall buy Jim that steamer he wanted so much yesterday - and I shall buy Eileen a new spade because hers has a broken handle.'

'Oh Granny, Granny, it was a good thing after all that you lost your necklace!' cried the children. 'You have got a feast of shrimps - and we shall have new toys!'

'And I have seen how kind my two children can be,' said Mummy, smiling. 'So we are all happy.'

Granny had a new clasp put on her necklace, and she still has it. She told me this story to tell to you. I do hope you like it!

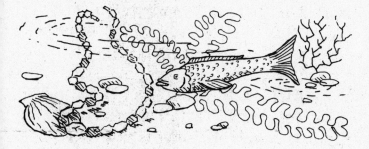

11

The Ho-Ho Goblins

Once upon a time the Ho-Ho goblins
laid a plan. They wanted to catch the
Skippetty pixies, but for a long time
they hadn't been able even to get near
them. Now they had thought of a
marvellous idea!

'Listen!' said Snicky, the head goblin.
'You know when the pixies sit down to
feast, in the middle of their dancing,
don't you? Well, they sit on toadstools!
And if *we* grow those toadstools we can
put a spell in them so that as soon as
the pixies sit down on them, they shoot
through the earth into our caves below
– and we shall have captured them
very nicely indeed!'

'A splendid idea!' said the other
goblins in delight. 'We'll do it!'

'Leave it all to me,' said Snicky. 'I

will go to them and offer to grow them toadstools for their dance much more cheaply than anyone else – and I will grow them just over our caves, as I have said – then the rest is easy.'

So the goblins left it to Snicky. As soon as he heard that the invitations to the party had been sent out, he went knocking at the door of Pinky, one of the chief pixies.

'What do you want?' asked Pinky,

opening the door. She did not like the Ho-Ho goblins.

'Dear Madam Pinky,' said Snicky, bowing low, 'I come to ask you if you will kindly allow me to grow the toadstools for you for your dance.'

'How much do you charge?' asked Pinky.

'One gold piece for one hundred toadstools,' said Snicky.

'That is very cheap,' said Pinky. 'We had to pay three gold pieces last time.'

'Madam, they will be excellent toad-stools, strong and beautiful,' said Snicky. 'Please let the Ho-Ho goblins do them for you.'

'Well, I don't like the goblins, but that's no reason why I shouldn't have their toadstools,' said Pinky. 'Very well. You shall make them for our dance. We want them in the wood under the oak tree.'

'Madam, it is very damp there,' said Snicky. 'It would be better to grow them under the birch tree.'

Snicky knew quite well that under the birch tree lay the caves of the Ho-Ho goblins. He must grow the toadstools there, or the goblins would not be able to catch the pixies as planned.

'Oh, very well,' said Pinky. 'It can't make much difference whether the dance is held under the oak or the birch. We want the toadstools on the next full-moon night, Snicky.'

Snicky ran off full of glee. He had got what he wanted! He called a meeting of the others, and told them.

'Now,' he said. 'Not one of you must tell a word of this to anyone, for we must keep it a secret. We must get a runaway spell from Witch Grumple, and each toadstool must be rubbed with the spell. Then, at a magic word, all the toadstools, with the pixies on

them, will rush away through the ground straight to our caves below.'

'Hurrah!' cried the Ho-Ho goblins. 'They will be our servants at last.'

Snicky went to ask Witch Grumple for the spell. She was not at home. Her servant, a big black cat with green eyes, said that his mistress had gone walking through the fields to collect some dew shining in the new moon.

'I'll go and meet her,' said Snicky. So off he went. He found the witch walking by the hedges that ran round the cornfield. She had a dish in which she was collecting the silvery dew-drops.

'Good evening, Witch Grumple,' said Snicky. 'May I speak secretly with you for a moment?'

'Certainly,' said the witch. She looked all around to see that no one was about. 'Come into the corn,' she said. 'No one will hear us then. What is it you want?'

'I want a runaway spell,' said Snicky.

'What will you give me for it?' asked the witch.

'I'll give you two Skippetty pixies for servants,' said Snicky.

'Don't be silly,' said Grumple. 'You haven't any pixies to give away!'

'I soon shall have if you let me have the runaway spell,' said Snicky.

'Tell me what you are going to do with it,' said Grumple.

'No,' said Snicky; 'someone might hear me.'

'There is no one to hear you,' said Grumple. 'Tell me, or I will not let you have the spell.'

So Snicky told Grumple exactly what he was going to do to capture the pixies, and she shook with laughter.

'Splendid!' she said. 'I shall be glad to see those stuck-up little pixies punished. Come back with me and I'll give you the spell.'

Now all would have gone well with the Ho-Ho goblin's plan – if someone hadn't overheard the secret that Snicky told Grumple. Who heard it? You will never guess.

The corn heard it with its many,

many ears! Grumple had quite forgotten that corn has ears. They were
ripe ears too, ready to catch the
slightest whisper. They listened to all
that Snicky said, and, because they
liked the Skippetty pixies, they wanted
to warn them. So the next time the
wind blew the corn, it whispered its
secret to the breeze.

'Snish-a-shish-a-shish-a-shish!' went
the corn as the wind blew over it. The
wind understood its language and
listened in astonishment to the tale the
corn told of Snicky's plan. Off it went
to the pixies at once.

When Pinky heard of Snicky's plan,
she went pale with rage and fear. To
think how that horrid, horrid goblin

had nearly tricked her! Off she sped to the Fairy King and told him everything. He laughed and said, 'Aha! Now we shall be able to play a nice little trick on Snicky himself!'

So, on the night of the dance, all the pixies laughed and talked as if they had no idea of the toadstool trick. The goblins crept around, watching and waiting for the moment when they could send the toadstools rushing down below to their caves.

Suddenly Pinky stopped the dance and said, 'Let's play musical chairs for a change! Goblins, come and join in!'

The Ho-Ho goblins felt flattered that they should be asked to play with the pixies. So they all came running up. Pinky pointed to the toadstools that Snicky had grown for them.

'Those shall be the chairs,' she said. 'When the music stops, everyone must sit down if he can!'

The band began again. Pixies and goblins ran merrily round the toadstools – but every pixie had been

warned not to sit down, but to let the
goblins take the toadstools. So, when
the music stopped, the goblins made a
rush for the toadstools and sat heavily
down on them meaning to win the
game of musical chairs.

As soon as Pinky saw the goblins
sitting on the toadstools, she called out
a magic word at the top of her voice.
Those toadstools sank down through
the ground at top speed! You see,
Snicky had rubbed them hard with a
runaway spell the night before – and
Pinky knew the word to set them off!

To the goblin's great fright, the toadstools rushed down to their cave – and there, calmly waiting for them were the soldiers of the Fairy King. As the toadstools came to rest in the caves, each goblin was surrounded by three soldiers. They were prisoners!

'That was a fine trick you planned, wasn't it?' grinned a soldier. 'But not so fine when it's played on yourselves! Come along now, quick march!'

Off the goblins went – and for a whole year they had to work hard for the pixies, to punish them for trying to play such a horrid trick.

And to this day they don't know who gave their secret away – although people say that if you listen to the corn as it whispers in the wind, you can, if you have sharp ears, hear it telling the wind all about Witch Grumple and Snicky the goblin. 'I'd love to hear it, wouldn't you?

12

The Kind Little Dog

Once upon a time there was a little dog called Sandy. He belonged to a little girl. Her name was Susan, and she and Sandy loved one another very much.

Susan and Sandy were staying by the sea. Every day Susan dug in the

sand and Sandy dug too. He dug with his paws, and Susan dug with her spade. But Sandy managed to dig just as big holes as Susan.

One afternoon Susan lay down on the sand and fell fast asleep. It was hot and she was sleepy. Sandy wasn't sleepy at all. He wandered off by himself to sniff about over the beach. perhaps someone had left a bag of old sandwiches about. Sandy thought he would like those!

He came up to an old man who was sitting reading a newspaper. If Sandy had stopped to look at the old man's face he would have seen what a cross, bad-tempered face it was. But sandy didn't look at it. He had found something rather exciting.

In the sand by the old man's chair
Sandy had smelt a nice smell. He
began to dig to see what it was. It came
from a cardboard box that had had a
pork pie in it. The smell had been there.
Sandy got very excited indeed.

He scraped at the sand and he
scraped. He dug quite a big hole – and
oh, my goodness, what do you think
happened? He dug the hole rather near
to one leg of the old man's deck-chair –
and suddenly the chair tilted sideways
and went into the hole. The old man
nearly fell out – and he *was* cross! He
glared round at Sandy and then he
caught hold of him by his collar. He
shook him well and hit him on the
head. Sandy yelped and ran away. The
man picked up some big stones and
threw them after the little dog. Two hit

him. One hurt his hind leg and the other hit his head.

Poor little dog Sandy! He couldn't understand why anyone should be so unkind to him. He ran to Susan, who had wakened up and was very cross and upset to see her little dog so unkindly treated. She hugged him and looked at his leg and his head where the stones had hit him.

She took him home and bathed his leg, because it was bleeding. Sandy did like being petted and fussed. It was very nice.

The next day Susan and Sandy went down once more on the beach. It was such a windy day. The hair on Sandy's back blew up in the wind and the hair on Susan's head blew up too.

Susan looked to see if the cross old man was there. He was. He sat in his chair reading his paper, his straw hat on his head. And suddenly, as Susan looked at him, the wind came along and whipped that straw hat right off the old man's head. Wheeoo!

The hat rolled over the sand. It went as fast as a ball, for the wind was having a lovely game with it. Susan wondered if she should run after it – then she remembered how unkind the man had been to her little dog, and she didn't move a step. But Sandy did! He tore after that hat, barking to it to come back!

But the hat went on and on – and the wind laughed to itself as it blew it farther and farther away! Wheeeoo! Wheeeee! Wheeeeoo!

And then, just as Sandy was about to pounce on that hat, the wind blew it into the sea! It rolled right through the little waves till a big wave caught it and filled it with water. But the hat bobbed up again, floating on the sea merrily.

'Oh, my nice new hat!' groaned the old man. 'It's gone for good now!'

Sandy barked loudly. He splashed into the sea and raced through the little waves after the hat. But it was in deep water. Still, Sandy could swim! He swam with all his four short little legs, keeping his head above the water, though the biggest waves splashed into his face and wet his ears and nose. The hat bobbed on. Sandy swam faster and faster.

He knew quite well it belonged to the unkind man who had hit him and thrown stones at him. But, Sandy's little doggy heart was too big and kind to think of that. He wanted to get that hat for the man – so on and on he swam!

130

Susan called him. She was afraid he might drown in such deep water. 'Come back, Sandy, come back!' she cried. But the wind and the sea made such a noise that Sandy couldn't hear her. He saw the hat quite near. He swam hard with all four legs. He reached the hat at last – and snapped at it with his white teeth. He had it, he had it! Clever little dog, Sandy!

He turned and swam back to the shore, tired and panting. he held the hat firmly in his mouth. He came to the sands at last and shook himself. He ran to the old man and laid the hat down at his feet, his tail wagging away fast.

'Thank you, little dog,' said the old man, picking up his hat. He beckoned to Susan. She came running over.

'Your dog has done me a good turn,' said the man. 'Would you like a nice new tenpenny piece? I have one in my pocket?'

'No, thank you,' said Susan.

'Well, what would you like?' asked the man. 'Tell me, and I will do it for you?'

'Do you know what I would like?' said Susan, looking up at the old man. 'I would just like you to promise me something, please. You hurt my little dog yesterday, and I was sad. Will you please promise me not to hurt any dogs again? That would be better than tenpence. You were unkind to my little dog, but he wasn't unkind to you. He did his best to help you.'

The old man stared at Susan. 'Well, well, well,' he said at last. 'It's the first time I've been told that a dog can behave better than I can. But I do believe you are right. I'll give you my

133

promise, little girl. I will never be unkind to dogs again.'

He patted Sandy, and Sandy wagged his tail hard again. Then the old man, quite forgetting that his hat was wet, put it on his head and walked off. Susan watched him go. Then she hugged Sandy.

'You are a good, kind little dog, and I love you!' she said. 'I don't expect that old man will ever hurt a dog again.'

And, do you know, he didn't! Sandy had taught him a lesson, hadn't he?

13

Sally Simple's Spectacles

Sally Simple had a fine pair of spectacles. They sat on her round nose beautifully, and looked very grand, for the glass was square, not round, and the frame was bright green. Sally Simple felt very fine indeed when she wore her spectacles. She didn't really need to wear any, for her eyes were perfectly good – but when she had seen those grand green spectacles in a shop, with their square glass, she had fallen in love with them and had bought them!

One day Sally went to a sewing-meeting. She set off, in her best green blouse with the yellow buttons, and her spectacles in a case. It was raining hard, so Sally put up her umbrella and went squelching through the mud.

There were a lot of people at the sewing-meeting. Old Dame Twinkle was there, and Mother Hubbard. Mrs Pippitty was there and Mrs Popoff. The meeting was quite crowded. Sally Simple was pleased.

'There will be all the more people to see my beautiful glasses,' she thought to herself. She sat down at a table, and put her umbrella beside her, for she was always afraid that someone else might take it if she put it into the umbrella stand.

Sally took out her spectacle case and opened it. She put her marvellous green spectacles on her round nose and looked to see if anyone was admiring them.

'Goodness, Sally!' said Dame Twinkle, her shining face all over smiles, 'what do you want spectacles for? Your eyes are as good as mine any day!'

'And what queer ones they are!' said Mother Hubbard.

'They cost a lot of money,' said Sally Simple, offended. 'They are the very latest fashion. Your bonnet, Mother Hubbard, is much queerer than my spectacles. It must be more than fifty years old.'

'Now, now!' said Mrs Popoff. 'No quarrelling, please. I am sure, Sally, that your spectacles will help you to sew beautifully!'

Sally put her glasses firmly on her nose and bent over her work. 'Everyone is jealous of me because I have such fine spectacles,' she thought. 'Well, let them be!'

Now Sally soon found that she could see better without the new spectacles than with. They were not made for *her* eyes, and they hurt them. What a nuisance! Sally began to blink and wink – but she did not want to take them off – no! What would be the good of buying them if she didn't wear them?

But when tea-time came Sally Simple took them off and put them on the table. She did like to see properly all that she was eating. She ate tomato sandwiches and cucumber sandwiches. She ate brown bread and butter and strawberry jam. She ate a ginger bun, a chocolate cake, and two slices of cherry

cake – and she drank four cups of tea.
So she enjoyed herself very much, and
laughed and joked with the rest.

But when tea was over, Sally thought
she would put her beautiful glasses on
again, and she looked for them – but,
dear me, they were gone!

'I put them on the table, just here!'
said Sally Simple, and she looked
everywhere on the table for her lovely
glasses. But they weren't there! She

looked in the cotton box. She looked among the scissors. She unrolled the roll of cloth nearby. But nowhere could she see her precious glasses!

'Has somebody taken my glasses?' asked Sally in a loud voice. 'They have gone! I simply must have them to wear whilst I am sewing.'

'*I* haven't seen them,' said Mother Hubbard.

'Nor have I,' said Dame Twinkle.

'I expect Sally's got them herself,' said Mrs Pippitty. 'Have you looked in your pocket, Sally?'

'Of course I have,' said Sally. 'I've looked everywhere!'

'They may be on the floor,' said Mrs Popoff. So everyone put down scissors, sewing, and needles, and hunted on the floor for Sally's spectacles. But they were nowhere to be seen. It was really most mysterious. The empty case was in Sally's pocket – but the glasses seemed to have disappeared completely.

There is only one thing I can think,' said Sally, pursing up her lips.

'And what is that?' asked Dame Twinkle.

'Well – I think *one* of you has taken my new spectacles,' said Sally. 'I know *some* people felt jealous of them! Now, who is it! I tell you, I must really have them back, because they cost a lot of money.'

'Sally! You should not say that one of us has taken your silly glasses,' said Mother Hubbard crossly.

'They are *not* silly,' said Sally.

'They are – *very!*' said Mother Hubbard.

'They are *not!*' said Sally, going red.

'Now, now!' said Mrs Popoff. 'I expect they will turn up soon. Shall we all open our work-bags and see if the glasses have got in there by mistake?'

So each one opened her basket and tipped out cottons and silks and needles – but nobody had those glasses, it seemed. It was most peculiar.

'Well, I simply don't know where they can have gone to, Sally,' said Mrs Pippitty. 'Let us get on with our work again now. We have wasted quite enough time.'

'Well, I shall not stay here a minute more,' said Sally Simple in a rage. '*Someone* has my glasses – my beautiful green glasses – and I shall go home and not come to this horrid, nasty sewing-meeting any more!'

'Don't be silly, Sally,' said Mother Hubbard.

But Sally's mind was made up. She was not going to stay and sew without her glasses! She got up from her seat and took down her mackintosh from its peg. She put it on, and buttoned it right up to her neck. She set her hat straight. She put on her gloves and buttoned them. Then she took up her umbrella and walked to the door.

'Sally, don't go in a temper like this,' said Mrs Popoff kindly. 'It is foolish of you. Your glasses will turn up somewhere, and then you will be sorry.'

'I shall *not* be sorry!' said Sally, who was most upset. She opened the door. It was pouring with rain. Dear, dear, what wet weather!

'And I hope that whoever has my glasses will be WELL PUNISHED!' said Sally. She opened her umbrella – and oh, my goodness me, out of it fell something that shone and glittered – something that fell to the ground – and smashed into a hundred shining little pieces – Sally's beautiful green glasses!

They had slipped off the table into her umbrella, as it stood by her knee at tea-time. No one had seen them slip off – and no one had thought of looking in

Sally's own umbrella! Everyone stared - and stared.

'Well, Sally!' said Mother Hubbard, at last, 'your wish has come true. You said that you hoped that whoever had your glasses would be well punished - and you were the one that had them - and you have been punished because they are broken.'

Poor Sally Simple! She did feel so ashamed of herself - and there were her lovely glasses, smashed to bits - all because she had walked out in a temper! Tears poured down Sally's cheeks. Kind Mrs Popoff saw them and came running to Sally. She put her arms round her.

'Never mind,' she said. 'You look *so* much nicer without spectacles, Sally, dear. And besides, I am sure they were bad for your eyes, because they made you wink and blink. So don't worry any more. Come and take your things off again, and do a bit more sewing.'

Sally was so ashamed of herself that all she wanted to do was to go home -

but Mrs Popoff was so kind that she went back again into the room and took off her things.

'I beg everybody's pardon,' she said in a little voice. 'It was very foolish and wrong of me.'

And after that Sally Simple didn't buy any more spectacles – because her eyes really were very good indeed. She is much nicer now, so perhaps it was a good thing those green glasses were snashed to bits. What do *you* think?

14

Poor Captain Puss!

Ronald and Jill were very lucky. In the summer they always went to Cliffsea, where their father had a house almost on the beach. It was such fun to wake up in the morning and hear the waves splashing on the sands not far off.

All the household went to Cliffsea in the summer, even Toby the dog and Patter the kitten! No one was left behind. Toby liked the sea very much, and Patter loved playing about in the sand.

Next door to the children's house was a smaller one, and two cats and a dog lived there with their mistress. The dog was called Spot, and the cats were called Sooty and Snowball, so you can guess what they were like to look at.

Toby, Patter, Sooty, Snowball, and

Spot were soon good friends. Patter the kitten had a fine time with them. They made quite a fuss of her because she was the smallest and youngest.

So she was rather spoilt, and she became vain and boastful. Ronald and Jill spoilt her too, and said she was just the cleverest kitten they had ever seen.

'See how she runs after my ball!' said Ronald, as Patter raced over the sand to get his ball.

'See how Patter plays with this bit of seaweed!' said Jill. 'She fetched it from the rocks for me Ronald. She *is* a clever kitten! She can do simply anything!'

Patter felt very clever indeed. She went about with her head in the air and began to think that the other animals were rather stupid.

148

But there was one thing she would *not* do! She wouldn't go paddling and bathing with the children as Toby and Spot did. No – she hated the water. She thought it was simply horrid to get her dainty little feet wet.

Then one day Ronald and Jill brought down a beautiful big ship to the beach. It was a toy one, but was so big that Toby and Spot could almost get into it. Ronald and Jill played happily with it all the morning, and sailed it on the rock-pools that were spread all over the beach.

When they went indoors to dinner the five animals crowded round the pretty boat.

'I wish I could sail in it!' said Toby. 'I'd love to sail in that pool. I would make a good captain!'

'So would I,' said Spot, wagging his tail and sniffing at the boat as it stood half-upright in the sand.

'I would make the *best* captain!' said Patter the kitten boastfully. 'Ronald and Jill are always saying what a clever kitten I am. I am sure I could sail this ship much better than any of you!'

'Why, Patter, you little story-teller!' cried Snowball, 'you know how you hate to get your feet wet! You wouldn't be any good at all at sailing a boat.'

'Yes, I should,' said Patter crossly. 'I know just what to do. You pull that thing there – the tiller, it's called – and the boat goes this way and that. I heard Ronald say so!'

'You don't know anything about it at all,' said Sooty scornfully. 'You are just showing off as usual!'

'I'm not!' mewed Patter angrily. She jumped into the boat and put her paw on the tiller. 'There you are,' she said. 'This is what makes the boat go!'

The others laughed at her. They were sure that Patter would hate to go sailing really. They ran off and left her. She stared after them crossly, and then she lay down in the boat in the warm sunshine. She wouldn't go and play with the others if they were going to be so horrid to her. No, they could just

Poor Captain Puss!

play by themselves!

Patter shut her eyes, for the sun was very bright. She put her nose on her paws and slept. She didn't hear the sea coming closer and closer. She didn't know the tide was coming in! It crept up to the boat. It shook it a little. But Patter slept on, dreaming of sardines and cream.

Toby, Spot, Sooty and Snowball wondered where Patter was. They couldn't see her curled up in the ship. They thought she had gone indoors in a huff.

'She is getting to be a very foolish little kitten,' said Toby. 'We must not take so much notice of her.'

'It is silly of her to pretend that she would make such a good sailor,' said Sooty. 'Everyone knows that cats hate the water.'

'Well, we won't bother about her any more,' said Snowball. 'She's just a little silly. Let's lie down behind this shady rock and have a snooze. I'm sleepy.'

So they all lay down and slept. They

were far away from the tide and were quite safe.

But Patter was anything but safe! The sea was all round the ship now! In another minute it would be floating! A great big wave came splashing up the beach – and the ship floated! There it was, quite upright, floating beautifully!

The rock-pool disappeared. It was now part of the big sea. The ship sailed merrily on it. It bobbed up and down on the waves.

Patter suddenly woke up, and wondered why things bobbed about so. She sat up and saw that she had fallen asleep in the boat – and when she looked over the side, what a shock for her! She was sailing on the sea! Big waves came and went under the boat. The beach was far away!

'Miaow!' wailed Patter. 'Miaow! I'm out at sea! I'm afraid! I shall drown!'

But no one heard her. The sea was making such a noise as the tide came in. Patter forgot how she had boasted about being a good sailor. She forgot that she had boasted she could sail the boat quite well. She just clung on to the side and watched with frightened eyes as the green waves came and went.

Ronald and Jill suddenly remembered that they had left their sailing ship on the beach.

'My goodness! And the tide's coming in!' said Ronald in dismay. 'Quick, Jill, we must go and see if our boat is safe!'

They ran from the house to the beach – and then saw that the tide was right in. And, far away, on the big waves, floated their beautiful ship, all by itself!

'Look!' cried Jill. 'There it is! But there is someone in it. Who is it Ronald?'

Ronald stared hard. Then he shouted out in surprise: 'Why, it's Patter the kitten! Yes, it really is! Look at her in the boat Jill!'

'Oh, the clever thing!' cried Jill, who really thought that the kitten was sailing the ship. 'Oh, whoever heard of a kitten sailing a boat before! Spot,

Toby, come and look at Patter sailing our ship!'

Spot, Toby, Sooty and Snowball awoke in a hurry and ran to see what all the excitement was about. When they saw Patter the kitten out in the boat, rocking up and down on the sea, they could hardly believe their eyes.

'Captain Puss is sailing the boat,' said Jill. 'Captain Patter Puss! Isn't she clever!'

But Spot didn't think that Patter was as clever as all that. His sharp ears had caught a tiny mew – and that mew was very, very frightened. It wasn't the voice of a bold captain – it was the mew of a terrified kitten!

'I believe she went to sleep in the boat and the tide came and took it away,' wuffed Spot to Toby.

'Well, it will do her good to see that she isn't such a marvellous captain after all!' Toby barked back.

'She *would* be silly enough to fall asleep just when the tide was coming in,' said Sooty.

'All the same, she's very frightened,' said Snowball, who had heard two or three frightened mews.

'Sail the boat to shore, Patter!' shouted Ronald. 'Sail her in! We don't want to lose her!'

But Patter was much too frightened to pay any attention to what was said. She just went on clinging to the side of the boat. She felt very ill, and wished that she was on dry land.

Spot was quite worried. He knew what a little silly Patter really was – but all the same he thought she had been frightened quite enough. What could be done?

'I'll go and fetch her,' wuffed Spot, and he plunged into the sea. He swam strongly through the waves, which were now getting quite big, for the wind had blown up in the afternoon. Up and down went Spot, swimming as fast as he could, for he was really rather afraid that the ship might be blown over in the wind – and then what would happen to Patter!

The boat was a good way out. The wind blew the white sails strongly. The waves bobbed it up and down like a cork. Patter was terribly frightened, for once or twice she thought the boat was going over.

And just as Spot got there, the wind gave the sails such a blow that the boat *did* go over! Smack! The sails hit the sea, and the boat lay on its side. Splash! Poor Patter was thrown into the water. She couldn't swim – but Spot was there just in time! He caught hold of her by the skin of her neck, and holding her head above the water, he swam back to shore. The ship lay far out to sea on its side.

Spot put poor, wet, cold Patter on the sand, and shook himself. Patter mewed weakly.

The others came running up to her. 'Well, you didn't make such a good sailor after all,' said Sooty.

'Don't say unkind things now,' said Snowball. 'Patter has been punished enough. Come into the house, Patter, and sit by the kitchen fire and dry yourself.'

Ronald and Jill watched the five animals running into the house. Then Ronald turned up his shorts and went wading into the water to see if he could get back his boat.

'That kitten was silly!' he said. 'She took my boat out to sea, couldn't sail it back again, made it flop on to its side, and fell out herself! She isn't so clever as she thinks.'

159

He got back his boat and went to dry the sails in the kitchen. Patter was there, sitting as close to the fire as she could, getting dry.

'Hullo, Captain Puss!' said Ronald. 'I don't think you are much of a sailor!'

'No, she is just a dear, silly little kitten,' said Jill.

Patter felt ashamed. How she wished she hadn't boasted about being a good sailor! She wondered if the others would ever speak to her again.

They did, of course, and as soon as they found that she wasn't boastful any more they were as good friends as ever.

But if Patter forgets, they laugh and say, 'Now, Captain Patter! Would you like to go sailing again?'

15

Simon's Clean Handkerchief

'Mother,' said Simon one day, 'the teacher says I *must* take a clean handkerchief to school each day.'

'Good gracious me, I should think so,' said his mother. 'You know where your clean handkerchiefs are, don't you, Simon? Well, just see you take one each morning.'

So the next morning Simon started off with a nice clean handkerchief. He was so pleased to have it that he carried it in his hand. He meant to show it to his teacher as soon as he got to school.

But on the way Simon had to climb over a stile. He laid his handkerchief carefully down on the top, and climbed over. And will you believe it, he left his handkerchief on the stile. When he got to school the teacher said: 'Did you remember your handkerchief today, Simon?'

'Yes,' said Simon – but, dear me, it wasn't in his hands and it wasn't in his

pockets. 'I've left it on the stile,' said Simon. 'Bother!'

As he came home from school he looked for his handkerchief – and there it was on the ground, in rags! Daisy the cow had come along and seen it on the stile. She had given it a chew and then spat it out. It was no use at all as a handkerchief now!

That afternoon Simon took another handkerchief from his drawer. 'I will tie a knot in it to remind myself to hold on to it all the way to school,' he thought. So he tied a big knot in the corner. Then off he went.

He climbed over the stile safely, his handkerchief in his hand. He went on jogging along happily. Suddenly he saw a butterfly and he went after it. It settled on a flower. Simon put down his handkerchief, and crept up to the butterfly. He pounced – but the butterfly was gone, flying high into the air!

'Bother!' said Simon, and skipped off to school. He had left his clean handkerchief on the ground.

'Where is your handkerchief, Simon?' asked the teacher.

'Oh,' said Simon proudly, 'do you know Miss Brown, I tied a knot in it to remind me to bring it. Wasn't that clever of me!'

'Well, where is it?' asked Miss Brown.

Well, of course, Simon couldn't find it anywhere! He had left it behind on the grass.

Miss Brown was cross with him.

'You are a naughty little boy,' she said. 'Now just remember it tomorrow, please.'

So the next morning Simon took another handkerchief from his pile. He hadn't been able to find the one he had

164

left on the grass, because the wind had blown it away.

'Now I really and truly will remember to take my handkerchief this time!' said Simon. 'I will not let it leave my hand all the way to school.'

Just as he started off, his mother called him. 'Simon, dear! Post this letter for me on your way, will you?'

'Certainly, Mother!' said Simon. He took the letter and ran off. He wondered if he remembered his six times table, because he knew Miss Brown was going to hear it that morning. So he began to say his tables:

'Six times one are six,
Six times two are twelve.'

As he was saying his tables he came to the pillar-box, red and shining in the roadway. He ran up to it, saying his tables all the time, and was proud to think he knew the whole of six times. But do you know what he did? He posted his handkerchief instead of his mother's letter! Oh, Simple Simon, whatever is anyone to do with you!

166

'Well, Simon,' said his teacher, as he ran into school. 'I hope you've got your handkerchief today!'

'Yes Miss Brown,' said Simon proudly. 'I kept it in my hand all the time – look!'

He handed her – his mother's letter! Miss Brown stared in surprise.

'But this is a letter, not a handkerchief Simon,' she cried.

'Oh my, oh my!' groaned poor Simon, looking at it. 'I must have posted my handkerchief! Yes – that's what I did!'

'Simon, I shall be very cross with you soon,' said Miss brown. 'Please do try and bring a clean handkerchief this afternoon. I will give you one more chance.'

So Simon once more took a clean handkerchief from his drawer that afternoon. He put it into his pocket. He thought it would be safer there than in his hand! Off he started to school. But on the way he fell down. His knee bled, and his hands were covered with mud. Poor Simon! He took out his hand-

kerchief and scrubbed his hands. He wiped his knee. Then on he went again. But it was not Simon's lucky day. He brushed against some wet paint, and his nice jersey was covered with blue! Out came the handkerchief again, and Simon wiped off the blue paint.

But he did arrive at school with his handkerchief, and proudly he showed it to Miss Brown.

'Simon! What a horrid, dirty smelly rag!' she cried. 'Surely it is not a handkerchief! Didn't I say you were to bring a *clean* handkerchief? Just see you do tomorrow morning, or I will be cross!'

Simon cried all the way home, and when he told his mother what had happened she was cross with him. And she was crosser still when she found that he had lost his hat that morning too!

'Simon, you are the silliest child I ever knew!' she cried. 'Now, look here – this is one of your father's handker-chiefs, for you have used all yours. As you have no hat and the sun is very hot I am going to knot each corner of the handkerchief and make a cap for you out of it. You will wear it to school, and, goodness me, surely you can't lose it if you've got it on your head.'

Simon was pleased to have a hand-kerchief cap. His father's handkerchief was big and red with white spots. He felt very grand going to school with such a fine red cap on.

But, bless us all, when he got to

school he had forgotten that he had the handkerchief on his head! When Miss Brown asked him to show her his clean handkerchief, Simon turned out his pockets. But there was no handkerchief there!

'Simon!' said Miss Brown, in an angry voice. 'Do you mean to tell me you've forgotten again!'

'No, Miss Brown,' said Simon. 'I did bring a handkerchief with me this time, I really did! But, oh dear, wherever is it?'

'Take off your cap and come indoors,' said Miss Brown, looking very cross.

Simon took off his red cap – and no sooner had he got it in his hands than he saw that it was his father's nice clean red handkerchief!

'Miss Brown, Miss Brown, here it is!' he cried. 'I was wearing it on my head – and it's quite clean. Look!'

'Well, if you aren't the silliest little boy!' said Miss Brown. 'You've only *just* saved yourself a telling-off. Now, in future Simon, ask your mother to *pin*

170

a clean handkerchief to your jersey each day – then perhaps you will be able to bring it safely to school, and I shall see it!'

So that is what Simon does now – but today his mother was away, so Simon found the safety-pin to pin on his handkerchief – but, oh dear, he made a mistake, and pinned on to his jersey the baby's best white coat. Whatever will Miss Brown say?

16

Don't Tell Anyone

George had a new suit and a new pair
of boots. His mother had just bought
the suit, and it fitted George beautifully. It was dark blue, and had a
waistcoat like his father's. George was
very proud of it.

'When can I wear it?' he asked his
mother.

'Tomorrow,' she said. 'Auntie Winnie
is coming to tea and you must be clean
and tidy then.'

So after dinner the next day George
put on his new suit. He tied his tie
neatly, and brushed his hair till it
shone. He put on his new boots and tied
the laces tightly. My, he did look
grand!

'Mother, could I have my watch to
wear today for a treat?' he asked.

He had a fine silver watch and chain that Uncle Dick had given him last Christmas. It was such a nice one that George hardly ever wore it for fear of losing it. But he did think it would be fine to wear with his grand new suit.

'Yes, you can wear it,' said Mother. So George took it out of its leather case and slipped the watch into his pocket, and slid the chain through a buttonhole to the pocket on the opposite side. Now he really felt as grand as could be!

'Can I go for a little walk?' he asked his mother. 'I won't dirty myself.'

'Very well,' said Mother. 'Just go down to the sea and back.'

George lived by the sea, and he never got tired of watching the big waves in winter-time, and the people that came to bathe and paddle in the summer-time. He set off down the road and soon came to the front, where many people walked up and down, enjoying the hot sunshine.

George walked along the front slowly. He hoped everyone was noticing how

174

fine he looked with his silver watch chain across the front. Dear me, it wasn't often he looked so grand! usually he was a very dirty, untidy little boy – but just for once he was quite different!

The tide was in and was splashing right against the wall. Some children were standing watching it, and with them was a small three-year-old girl. As George passed, the little girl suddenly slipped and fell splash into the sea below!

'Oh! Oh!' shrieked the other children. 'Mollie's in the sea! Oh, quick, Mollie's in the sea!'

George ran to the place where the little girl had fallen in. There she was, struggling in the deep sea below. Oh dear, would nobody come! There seemed to be nobody grown-up at all to come and save the little girl.

George could swim. He was the best swimmer in his class at school. He forgot about his best clothes, and before anyone knew what he was doing he had jumped straight into the waves below! He fell close by the choking little girl, and he caught hold of her. He began to swim with her to the steps. It was difficult because she would cling to

him so. But at last he got her safely to the steps and dragged her up.

The other children pulled her in, crying with fright. One of them saw how wet George was.

'How will you get dry?' she said.

'Don't tell anyone!' said George, shaking himself like a dog, and trying to squeeze the water out of his coat. 'This is my new suit and my mother would be so upset to see it wet. Don't tell anyone, will you! I'll try and dry it.'

By this time a crowd had collected and the little girl ws being dried and comforted. George was able to slip away. A man tried to stop him, but George wriggled off.

'Please don't tell anyone!' be begged. Then off he ran home. He crept in at the back gate. No one was about. Mother must have gone to meet Auntie Winnie. Good!

The little girl next door looked over the fence. 'Ooooh!' she said. 'How did you get wet like that? Won't your mother be cross?'

'Now *please* don't tell anyone!' said George. 'I want to try and dry my clothes before my mother comes home.'

He slipped indoors and ran up to his room. He took off all his wet things and squeezed the water out of them. And then he discovered something that made him stand still in horror. He had lost his lovely silver watch and chain!

'It must have fallen out of my pocket when I was swimming with that little girl to the steps,' said George. 'Oh, what a dreadful thing! I was so proud of that watch.'

The little boy was very unhappy about his lost watch and chain, but he had no time to stop and grieve about it. He really must dry his clothes before his mother came home!

He put on his dressing-gown and hurried down to the kitchen. He put all his clothes through the dryer to begin with, and then he stood the clothes-horse in front of the fire and spread out his clothes there. How long would it take them to dry? Oh, he did hope they

would be ready in time!

Mother had gone to meet Auntie Winnie at the railway station, and, as it was such a lovely afternoon they went down to the front for a walk. There they heard everyone talking about a brave boy who had jumped into the sea and saved a little girl from drowning. But nobody seemed to know who it was! The children who had been with the little girl knew who it was, but they said nothing, because George had begged them not to tell anyone.

Mother stayed with Auntie Winnie on the front by the sea until tea-time.

Then they made their way home.

And what was George doing? Well, his clothes were nearly dry, and he had put them on. They looked very queer – most crumpled and untidy – and his boots wouldn't dry at all, so he had had to put his old ones on. He didn't look at all nice, but it was the best he could do. He hoped Mother wouldn't notice.

Auntie Winnie was pleased to see him. Mother took one look at him and then turned away, vexed. How *could* George get his nice new suit all untidy and crumpled like that? It was too bad of him. George saw how vexed she looked, and he was unhappy. But Mother didn't scold him in front of Auntie Winnie.

'Show Auntie Winnie your silver watch and chain whilst I make the tea,' she said.

Poor George! He went very red, and didn't know what to say.

'I lost it this afternoon I'm afraid,' he said to Auntie Winnie.

Auntie Winnie wondered what was

the matter with George. He looked so
hot and untidy and unhappy. Perhaps
he wasn't well. She began to talk about
her walk along the front that afternoon.

'And do you know, George,' she said,
'everyone was talking about a brave
boy who had jumped into the sea and
saved a little girl from drowning this
afternoon!'

'Oh,' said George, going redder than
ever.

'Wasn't it brave of him?' said Auntie
Winnie. 'The little girl's mother does so
want to know who the little boy was, so
that she could thank him, but no one
seems to know. He ran off without even
giving his name. I wonder why!'

'Oh,' said George, going redder than
ever. This was dreadful.

Mother had been listening, and
watching George. She quickly went to
him and felt his coat. It was damp.

'George,' she said. 'Was it *you* who
jumped into the water after that little
girl?'

181

'Yes, Mother,' said George. 'But I quite forgot I had my new suit on when I did it. I just couldn't help it. And I've lost my watch and chain. I'm so unhappy about that. But, you see, there wasn't anyone else nearby who could swim, so I just had to jump in. I have tried to dry my clothes, but they wouldn't dry properly.'

'Oh, George!' said his mother, and to George's surprise she suddenly hugged him as if she would choke him.

'What do you suppose a new suit matters, or even a watch and chain, so long as you are brave? You have saved that little girl from drowning, and I don't mind about your suit a bit.'

George was surprised and pleased. His mother made him change his damp suit and put on his jersey and shorts. He felt much more comfortable. Auntie Winnie was so nice to him too. He began to feel much happier.

And to George's surprise he soon found that he was quite a hero. Somebody said that it was he who had jumped in to save the little girl, and people told him he was a fine brave boy. Nobody scolded him for spoiling his new suit or for losing his watch!

And what do you suppose the little girl's mother gave George the very next day? She sent him a *gold* watch to wear, with a strong leather chain so that it couldn't possibly be lost. He was so very proud.

'You deserve it, George,' said his mother. And his father said so too.

'Well,' said George, 'I tried not to let anyone know, because of my new suit – but it seems as if everyone knows my secret now. And I don't mind a bit, because you are all so nice to me.'

I've seen George's watch. It really is a fine one, I can tell you.

17

The Bad Cockyolly Bird

The Cockyolly bird lived in the nursery with the other toys. He was a colourful creature, with red plush wings, a yellow tail, and a green body. He could be wound up, and then he walked along in a jerky manner, saying 'Kack, kack, kack!' as he went.

Now the Cockyolly bird was a great nuisance. He was always picking up things that belonged to other people, and running off with them.

He ran off with the big doll's hair-ribbon, and she couldn't find it anywhere. Where do you suppose he had put it? He had stuffed it up the tap in the basin. When Nurse turned on the tap, out came the ribbon! She was so surprised.

He ran off with the baby doll's shoes. The baby doll had taken them off because they were rather tight, and she was enjoying herself, running about in her bare feet. And when she wanted her shoes they had gone.

'The Cockyolly bird took them,' said the clockwork mouse. 'I saw him. He has thrown them out of the window!'

So the baby doll had to climb down

the apple tree outside and go to hunt for her slippers in the dark. She didn't like it at all.

Everyone scolded the Cockyolly bird, but he only grinned and said 'Kack! If I could find some place to put your things so that you wouldn't find them so easily, I'd hide them away properly.'

And then one day the Cockyolly bird *did* find a place to put things – where do you suppose it was? You'll never guess! It was in the big money-box that stood up on the nursery mantelpiece.

He found a button off the soldier's tunic and he picked it up and popped it into the slit of the money-box. Clink! It fell in among the pennies and lay there. Then the Cockyolly bird hunted about for something else, and found the lamb's tail. It was always loose and had fallen off on to the floor.

The Cockyolly bird picked it up and flew off with it. He stuffed it into the money-box. Aha! The lamb wouldn't know where it had gone. He would look

for it all over the place.

Then the Cockyolly bird found the brooch belonging to the walking-doll. Dear me, he *was* pleased! He had once asked the walking-doll to lend it to him when he went to a party, and she wouldn't – so now she would be punished, thought the bad Cockyolly bird! He pushed it into the money-box. It fell inside with a little tinkling noise.

But the worst thing he did was to take the teddy bear's glass eye. The bear had two beautiful eyes, both made of brown glass, round and shining. But one was loose, and sometimes came out. Then it had to be stuck in again.

The teddy bear wanted to romp about one night, so he took his loose eye out and laid it carefully down on a chair in the doll's house. That was where the Cockyolly bird found it. He picked it up in his beak and flew off with it at once. Clink! It went into the money-box.

Oh, what a to-do there was when the teddy bear found his eye gone! 'I know that wicked Cockyolly bird has taken

it,' he cried. 'Oh, I know he has!'

The toys surrounded the Cockyolly bird and shouted at him:

'Where's the teddy bear's eye?'

'Where's the walking-doll's brooch?'

'Where's the lamb's tail?'

'Where's the soldier's button?'

'Aha! Oho! Where *you* won't be able to get them,' grinned the Cockyolly bird. 'They are all in the money-box.'

The toys stared at one another in dismay. In the money-box! Why, that was always locked – they would never be able to get anything out of that.

'Oh, you bad, wicked Cockyolly bird!' shouted everyone in a rage. The Cockyolly bird flung back his head and laughed and laughed and laughed. He did like to see the toys so angry. As he laughed, his key came loose, and suddenly it dropped to the floor. Clang!

In a trice the baby doll caught it up in her hand. She raced to the nearest chair. She climbed up it, she climbed up to the back. She jumped from there to the mantelpiece – and she ran to the money-box. She dropped the Cockyolly bird's key into the slit in the money-box. Clang!

Everyone stared. The Cockyolly bird broke into loud wailing.

'Kack! Kack! What have you done with my key? When I am run down I shan't be able to be wound up. I shan't be able to walk, or fly, or peck. Oh, you wicked baby doll!'

'You deserve it,' said everyone at once. 'If you put things belonging to *us* in the money-box, why shouldn't we put in things belonging to *you*! It serves you right!'

So it did. When his clockwork ran down, there was no key to wind up the Cockyolly bird, so he just had to stand in his corner and glare at everyone, and wish and wish that he had never been so stupid as to tell people what a good hiding place the money-box was!

When Mother's birthday came the children who lived in the nursery opened their money-box to get out some money to buy Mother a present; and dear me, *how* surprised they were to find so many queer things inside.

'How did they get there?' they said to one another. But nobody knew.

The Cockyolly bird got his key back.

The teddy bear got his glass eye back, and all the others got their things back too.

'And just remember this, Cockyolly bird,' said the teddy bear, as he stuck in his glass eye once more, and glared at the bird with it, 'we shall only be too pleased to put your key in the money-box if you play any more tricks. So behave yourself in future.'

And now the Cockyolly bird is as good as gold. He did get such a shock when his key went into the money-box – he doesn't want it to happen again, you may be sure!